The Next Jump Forward in Fitness

Ken M. Solis, MD
Executive Director, Ropics,® Inc.

Leisure Press
Champaign, Illinois

Library of Congress Cataloging-in-Publication Data

Solis, Ken M., 1958-
  Ropics : the next jump forward in fitness / Ken M. Solis.
    p.   cm.
  Includes bibliographical references (p.   ).
  ISBN 0-88011-444-4
    1. Rope skipping.   2. Physical fitness.   I. Title.
  GV498.S67   1991
  796.2--dc20
                                                90-24893
                                                CIP

ISBN: 0-88011-444-4

Copyright © 1992 by Ken Solis.

Acquisitions Editor: Brian Holding
Developmental Editor: Holly Gilly
Managing Editor: Valerie Hall
Assistant Editor: Elizabeth Bridgett
Copyeditor: Sara Black
Proofreader: Dawn Levy
Production Director: Ernie Noa
Typesetters: Yvonne Winsor and Sandra
  Meier

Text Design: Keith Blomberg
Text Layout: Tara Welsch, Craig Ronto,
  and Kim Henris
Cover Design: Keith Blomberg
Cover Photo: Wilmer Zehr
Illustrations: Gretchen Walters
Interior Photos: Bruce Haug, Creative
  Photography
Printer: Versa Press

Printed in the United States of America

10   9   8   7   6   5   4   3   2   1

Leisure Press
A Division of Human Kinetics Publishers, Inc.
Box 5076, Champaign, IL 61825-5076
1-800-747-4457

Canada Office:
Human Kinetics Publishers, Inc.
P.O. Box 2503, Windsor, ON N8Y 4S2
1-800-465-7301 (in Canada only)

UK Office:
Human Kinetics Publishers (UK) Ltd.
P.O. Box 18
Rawdon, Leeds LS19 6TG
England
(0532) 504211

Dedication

For some time, a relatively small circle of people has known that rope jumping is an activity with vast, untapped potential. It's been, however, both a source of shared delight and a frustration trying to enlighten others about this misunderstood activity. This book is dedicated to the people who have encouraged or influenced me in the development of Ropics and shared my vision of what rope jumping can become. In alphabetical order:

Dan Adams—The first rope artist I met who taught me keystone techniques like Turn-Abouts and Double Unders.

Bill Budris—Coach of The Wizards jump rope team, coauthor of *The Jump Rope Primer*, and personal friend.

Richard Cendali—Dynamic founder and leader of the International Rope Skipping Organization.

Greg Cortopassi, Bruce Guettich, and Mag Hughes—Pioneers in their own activity—footbag—and a constant source of encouragement and inspiration.

Mike and Kathleen Hargarten—Business partners and close friends who share every peak and valley Deb and I traverse in making rope jumping work for more people.

Chris Hearne—Talented jump rope artist, instructor, and founder of his own jump rope program.

Bobby Hinds—Lifeline jump rope manufacturer, rope jumping enthusiast since his boxing days, and Ropics' first real backer.

Buddy Lee—World-class rope artist and wrestler.

Ken Pierce and Karen Greathouse—Fellow rope artists, promoters, and super people who worked hard promoting rope jumping in Los Angeles.

Eddie Race—A catalyst for rope jumping wherever he goes and a senior rope jumping dynamo who still doesn't know how to say, "I'm too old to try that."

Deborah Solis—My wife and dearest friend who often sets aside her first love—dance—just to advance Ropics one tiny step.

Debra Stefan—Dedicated instructor and rope artist who brings a touch of Vegas-style dance movement to every demonstration.

Contents

Preface

During its brief history, the fitness boom has evolved and broadened as quickly as a looming thunderhead. Since the 1970s, nearly every activity from running to weight training to dance-exercise has been revolutionized in the realms of research, equipment, apparel, and number of dedicated participants. One superb form of exercise, however, has lagged behind its peers. That exercise is rope jumping.

Rope jumping's delayed blossoming can be attributed to three basic reasons. First, despite its familiarity, rope jumping has been unjustly burdened with several dissuasive myths like "You must be coordinated to jump rope" and "Rope jumping is hard on the knees." Second, due to the scarcity of accurate information, even many exercise experts are unaware of rope jumping's profound and varied strengths. Finally, most people find traditional rope jumping to be too strenuous at that most critical time—the beginning.

Ropics® : The Next Jump Forward in Fitness was conceived to prod rope jumping into full bloom. *Ropics* dispels the myths and reveals that even self-proclaimed klutzes can master an amazing number of challenging techniques if they learn the necessary skills step by step.

Ropics also brings the unsurpassed strengths of rope jumping to light. If you are still searching for an exercise you can stick with, perhaps rope jumping's unmatched variety and compatibility with music will get you hooked. If you've found that other exercise programs make too many demands on your lifestyle, realize that rope jumping is inexpensive and portable and does not depend on weather conditions or special facilities. If you need an exercise that burns calories, improves your heart and lungs, or tones the muscles of the arms, chest, buttocks, and legs, this book is for you. If you are an aerobics instructor and looking for a way to add more diversity to your classes, consider adding a jump rope—an incredibly versatile prop. If you are an athlete or coach, rope jumping's ability to hone quickness, coordination, agility, rhythm, and timing will interest you. And, if you've given rope jumping a try but ran into a couple of problems, read on.

Perhaps most importantly, *Ropics* introduces you to the revolutionary program from which it takes its name. The Ropics program was developed over a period of 10 years and is based upon extensive experience, the latest in exercise science, and a dash of imagination. For the first time, rope jumping is made much less strenuous by incorporating unique Low-Impact Techniques (LITs) such as whirls, wraps, and catches throughout the workout. LITs require no jumping and therefore give budding jump rope enthusiasts an enjoyable way to catch their breath and rest their calves without stopping the rope. LITs also more than triple the variety available within rope "jumping" so that boredom becomes a complaint of the past. Avid participants and fascinated onlookers describe Ropics as exciting. In fact, some enthusiasts who have mastered Ropics regularly perform their rope jumping skills for appreciative audiences.

Of course, simply offering more techniques might only overwhelm those already intimidated by the thought of just trying to do a Front Cross. Therefore, Ropics carefully divides the numerous techniques according to level of difficulty and how they are executed. Besides increasing guidance, placing the numerous techniques into meaningful divisions provides the milestones you need to measure your progress and increase motivation. Sooner than you think, you'll have mastered Front Crosses and be eagerly looking for the next technique to conquer.

Ropics goes beyond revealing the many attributes of rope jumping and its novel program. You'll also learn

- over 30 basic to advanced jump rope techniques and variations, half of which require *no* jumping;
- how to modify the Ropics program for your particular age, fitness level, or goals;
- the advantages and disadvantages of different jump ropes;
- how to choose appropriate apparel, floor surface, shoes, and music; and
- strategies to keep you motivated from day 1 through year 10.

In summary, *Ropics® : The Next Jump Forward in Fitness* reveals how you can reap the benefits and excitement hidden inside the surprisingly versatile jump rope. It's time for your fitness to take a bold jump forward.

Acknowledgments

I thank Kathleen Hargarten, Eddie Race, Carol Roen, Deborah Solis, Bob Stenzel, Gloria Weckwerth, Kristin Willman, and Heidi Zarder for taking the time to model for this book.

In a book that depends so extensively on photography, I also thank Bruce Haug of Creative Photography for doing such an excellent and efficient job.

Special thanks go to Judy Clark, Kathleen Hargarten, and Deborah Solis for their valuable insights and critiques.

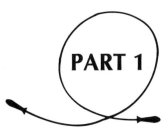

Getting a Jump on Fitness:

An Introduction to the Ropics® Exercise Program

As a physician and exercise expert, I'm frequently asked by my patients and friends, "Which is *the* best form of exercise?" My answer is simple: "It's whichever exercise you can prompt yourself to do regularly." More explicitly, it's whichever exercise or exercises you enjoy doing that fit your needs and lifestyle. This opening statement might sound self-defeating for a book whose sales depend on convincing you that rope jumping is the best exercise. This is the last time, however, that I will be so charitable. The rest of the book explains how and why rope jumping, or more accurately the Ropics approach to rope jumping, is the one exercise you will *want* to do regularly.

Chapter 1 reveals why I think rope jumping will become the apple of your eye. For centuries, rope jumping has been considered a form of recreation—not an arduous form of exercise. Despite its widespread staying power, however, many people, especially adults, do voice three common complaints about traditional rope jumping. Chapter 2 explains how the Ropics program addresses these complaints with surprisingly simple solutions. The importance of these solutions becomes apparent in chapter 3, which unveils the 20 benefits and advantages waiting to be tapped from

Note: If you are anxious to begin learning Ropics, please read at least the first section of chapter 4 and chapters 5 and 7 because they contain important information for maximizing the benefits of rope jumping and minimizing the risks of exhaustion and soreness.

this surprisingly versatile activity. Chapter 4 reviews how these benefits and advantages can apply specifically to you, whether you are young or old, a man or woman, an athlete or a budding exercise enthusiast.

CHAPTER 1

Where Rope Jumping Came From

The exact birthplace and birthdate of rope jumping have been lost somewhere among the larger events of history. But this fact hasn't prevented game historians from forwarding a few theories.

Rope Jumping Throughout History

One of the more intriguing theories about when and how rope jumping began proposes that ancient Egyptian and Chinese rope makers twirled and jumped over their ropes in order to recover loose hemp strands. Watchful children began imitating the practice for fun, and sailors exported the idea to youngsters in other lands. Whatever its true origin, we do know that long before recess was invented young Swedes were jumping over wicker cords, Spaniards twirled leather thongs, Hungarians used ropes made from plaited straw, and the natives of Barbados skipped over vines. It seems that young people would jump over whatever they could get their hands on.

Rope jumping was probably introduced to America in the 1600s by the Dutch settlers of New Amsterdam (modern-day New York). It may surprise you that for a long time rope jumping was strictly a boy's activity, at least in Western cultures. In fact, young girls were warned not to undertake such strenuous activity lest their blood vessels would burst! Fortunately, around the turn of the century, females realized that someone was pulling the wool over their eyes and began rope jumping with a vengeance.

The 1960s found jump ropes primarily in the hands of schoolgirls during playtime. Boys seemed happy to pursue team sports and leave rope jumping to the girls they thought of as "sissies." In the meantime, boxers in gymnasiums, rarely considered sissies, began to tout rope jumping as an exercise with superior athletic training properties. A few rope jumping luminaries such as Paul Smith and Frank Prentup went on to proclaim that rope jumping was a fun way for nearly anyone to stay fit and healthy. Their claims were not unfounded.

The late 1960s and the 1970s heralded a new era for exercise, including rope jumping. Although a variety of people had long insisted that exercise was important for physical health and emotional well-being, it wasn't until this time that the scientific evidence was persuasive enough to substantiate their claims. Health experts were then able to convince the public that our sedentary lifestyles were increasing our risk for heart disease, obesity, low back pain, certain types of cancer, osteoporosis, and depression, to name a few. Studies showed that regular exercise like rope jumping not only reduced the likelihood of these ailments, it even often reversed them.

Rope Jumping Today

Facts like the ones just discussed have not gone unnoticed by various organizations concerned about health and fitness. For instance, since 1978 the American Alliance for Health, Physical Education, Recreation and Dance (AAHPERD) and the American Heart Association (AHA) have vigorously promoted rope jumping through their sponsorship of Jump Rope For Heart (JRFH), the world's biggest event in rope jumping. JRFH takes place primarily in elementary schools throughout the United States and serves three primary purposes:

- To educate the participants and the community about heart disease
- To familiarize participants with habits like rope jumping that promote health
- To raise money for heart-related research

In the 1989-90 school year alone over 1.2 million participants from 13,500 schools raised $24 million. These figures make JRFH one of the most successful health awareness and fund-raising campaigns of any kind.

The success of JRFH goes even beyond the event itself. In response to the demands for demonstrations to promote the event, hundreds of jump rope teams sprouted up all over the country (see Figure 1.1). These largely elementary school-based dynamos travel to other schools, fairs, malls, sport half-time shows, and nearly all other venues to spread the word about JRFH, health, and fit-

Figure 1.1 Members of The Wizards jump rope team dance together while doing Double Dutch.

ness—and to dazzle audiences with an astounding variety of jump rope tricks and routines. By the way, boys as well as girls eagerly participate in these teams. The notion that rope jumping is for sissies has been rapidly losing ground.

When you get young people enthusiastically involved in an activity, it isn't long before they want to share their experiences, ideas, and techniques with their peers. The 1980s witnessed the birth of at least two youth-oriented jump rope organizations—The International Rope Skipping Organization and The Canadian Skipping Association. (You can learn more about these and other rope jumping groups in the appendix.)

Wrap-Up

Given the strides rope jumping has made in the past few decades, one might wonder, Is rope jumping approaching maturity? No, at best, it's still in its infancy. For example, despite JRFH's impressive success, it still has reached only 13% of the elementary schools. And the postadolescent age groups are virtually untouched. Indeed, it's puzzling that this highly touted activity should lack the level of competition, advances in equipment, and degree of organization enjoyed by newly developed activities like triathlons and aerobic dance. It's puzzling until you listen to the three complaints often voiced about traditional rope jumping—which Ropics handily addresses to make rope jumping attractive to *all* age groups.

CHAPTER 2

Why Ropics Is Better Than Traditional Rope Jumping

The reports that claimed rope jumping was an excellent exercise prompted me to try it as an alternative to running in the blustery winter of 1979. Like most people, however, I thought that rope jumping would be a supplemental exercise only—simply a side attraction when the Wisconsin weather didn't cooperate with my outdoor activities. Before long, however, I realized that rope jumping was a much more varied activity than I had first thought. Furthermore, I was having such a good time that I wondered why more people weren't rope jumping. Of course, I would occasionally run into other enthusiasts, and they were an important source of inspiration, ideas, and techniques for me. In general, however, we were lone wolves who jumped ropes in vacant gym corners while the pack played basketball, ran laps, or lifted weights.

During the 1980s, I became convinced of the jump rope's immense potential and began developing my own approach to rope jumping. Along the way, I also noted other people's reactions to this underappreciated activity. One thing nearly everyone agreed upon was that rope jumping was great at developing fitness. In the next breath, however, they would usually offer at least one of the following three complaints: 1) You have to be coordinated to jump rope, 2) it's too strenuous, or 3) it's boring. A few "minuses" were preventing many people from enjoying all of rope jumping's "pluses." I wanted to find a way to cancel the minuses while keeping, or even enhancing, the pluses. There are ways, and that's what the Ropics program is all about.

I originated the Ropics program over a decade ago, and it continues to evolve. The program's principles are based on a combination of scientific research, personal experience, and a dash of imagination. Just as importantly, Ropics has been further refined by the extensive teaching experience and creativity of my partners, Kathleen Hargarten, M.D., and Deborah Solis, M.F.A. It's interesting to note that Dr. Hargarten had already developed a rope jumping program with several features similar to Ropics when we decided to work together in 1988. The medical training we shared led us to develop similar solutions to the same complaints.

Traditional Complaint #1:
You Have to Be Coordinated to Jump Rope

This complaint is based on misunderstanding rather than fact. Rope jumping does not require remarkable coordination, but it is a skilled activity that you must learn properly. For example, with swimming, another skilled activity, you wouldn't just dive into the deep end of the pool on your first day in the water. You realize that you would thrash around, become exhausted, and possibly sink and drown. Instead, you practice at the shallow end of the pool first and seek proper instruction.

Ropics' Answer to Complaint #1:
Get Proper Instruction

As with swimming, the obvious answer is to *get proper instruction* before attempting to jump rope. Actually, anyone who is able to walk and talk at the same time already has ample coordination for rope jumping; however, you must learn the skills one step at a time. You crawled before running or doing the fox-trot, and you said "mama" before putting together a sentence or reciting Shakespeare. So it is with rope jumping. You need to practice the basic skills before jumping over the rope or doing tricks.

Furthermore, you must learn to perform each of the skills correctly and to use the right equipment. At times, there seems to be a conspiracy to keep rope jumping reserved only for the brazenly stubborn. In the past, magazines, jump rope packages, and even some instructional books have used inexperienced models who demonstrate rope jumping with many of the faults depicted in Figure 2.1.

Ropics uses only experienced models and presents techniques with careful step-by-step instruction as exemplified in Figure 2.2 and further explained in chapter 8. Using this method, we have not found anyone who couldn't jump rope well with a little practice.

Rope turned from shoulders

Feet kicking back

Bare feet

Jumping on wrong surface

Figure 2.1   An example of poor, even hazardous, rope jumping habits.

Ropics also gives helpful information on everything from the appropriate shoes to the strengths and weaknesses of different ropes. We've found that once armed with the correct information and proper instruction, anyone who can pass the walk-and-talk test has the coordination to jump rope. In fact, most have gone on to do the rope jumping equivalent of the fox-trot.

Traditional Complaint #2: Rope Jumping Is Too Strenuous

Both experience and research do support this complaint. Rope jumping at a typical rate, which is around 130 jumps per minute (JPM), expends the same amount of energy as running 9 to 10 minute miles or bicycling about 13 miles per hour. While these demands are rather modest, they are too high for the average inactive person to sustain continuously for very long. To make matters

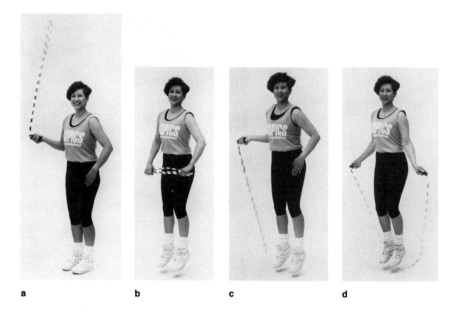

a   b   c   d

Figure 2.2   (a) Step 1: Learning how to turn the rope properly. (b) Step 2: Learning correct jumping form. (c) Step 3: Learning to jump in time to the rope. (d) Step 4: Putting it all together to jump over the rope.

worse, novices, who are inefficient at rope jumping, expend even more energy and end up feeling winded within minutes. Unfortunately, as Figure 2.3 shows, jumping slower than 145 JPM doesn't decrease the energy requirements because you must then jump higher to keep time with the turning rope. The higher jumps offset any energy saved by jumping more slowly.

Athletes and anyone else already accustomed to the aerobic requirements of traditional rope jumping also can encounter problems. Because their legs often aren't accustomed to jumping repeatedly, shin splints and sore calves can become a nuisance. In other words, active people who don't feel the least bit winded while jumping rope can wake up the next day with aching legs.

By the way, contrary to popular belief, rope jumping stresses the knees and hips much less than running does. Research by the Nike Company showed that the force to the legs from a similar activity—high-impact aerobic dance—was 2*g* while running was anywhere from 3 to 15*g*. That's 1-1/2 to 7-1/2 times less impact. Rope jumping is biomechanically like aerobic dance, because the participants jump and land on the balls of their feet in both activities.

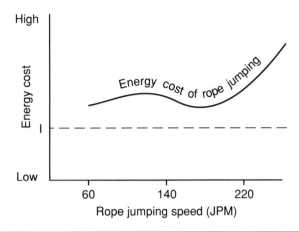

Figure 2.3   Point I on the vertical axis represents the maximum amount of energy an average inactive person can expend for 15 to 20 minutes. This graph illustrates that the energy cost of basic rope jumping, even at slow speeds, is too high for this type of person.

This means that the calves and shins absorb and control the impact. With running, runners usually land on their heels, and the force of impact is transmitted directly to the joints above. Our experience confirms these arguments. More than one of our students are unable to run due to knee injuries, but they can jump rope without problems.

Fortunately, the calves and shins adapt to new stresses much better than the knees and other joints. Nevertheless, something had to be done to decrease the demands rope jumping placed on beginners.

Ropics' Answer to Complaint #2: Use Low-Impact Techniques

Any healthy person can readily adapt to the moderate demands of rope jumping if the intensity of the sessions is gradually increased over time. Because jumping slowly is not the answer, it's necessary to alternate traditional rope jumping with a less strenuous form of exercise. Children simply stop jumping when tired and walk or stand. If they are using a long rope, they will allow someone else to jump or take turns spinning the rope until they've rested. Adults could choose a similar strategy, but Ropics offers a more provocative option: *Alternate brief periods of conventional jumping techniques with periods of Low-Impact Techniques.*

Low-Impact Techniques (LITs) form the cornerstone of Ropics, and as such, should be explained. LITs are any techniques that do not require the participant to jump over a rope (e.g., Figure 2.4). Therefore, they require less energy than jumping and place little stress on calves and shins. At the same time, they allow continued movement and involvement with the rope. This strategy is much better than starting and stopping repeatedly, which fosters the disparaging notion that the jump rope is too tough a task master.

To further illustrate the Ropics strategy, Figure 2.3 depicts the energy cost of basic rope jumping, which is too high for many beginners. With Ropics, budding jump rope enthusiasts spend a significant proportion of their workouts doing LITs and keep the jumping periods brief. Since LITs are less demanding than jumping, the average amount of energy spent during the workout decreases to the level where beginners don't feel exhausted. Then, as they become more fit and adept with the rope, they can decrease the LITs while increasing the jumping periods. This strategy increases the energy cost as illustrated in Figure 2.5 and keeps the participants challenged. Eventually, participants of nearly any age and fitness level can jump rope continuously for 15 minutes or more at a time without feeling winded or sore. Thus, LITs allow a

a   b

Figure 2.4   (a) A Figure-Eight and (b) a Waist Wrap—examples of Low-Impact Techniques.

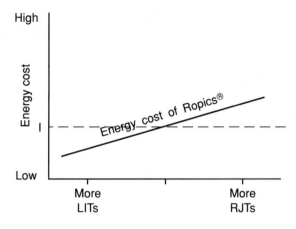

Figure 2.5   The energy cost of exercising with a jump rope can be decreased by incorporating Low-Impact Techniques (LITs) into the workout and increased by including more Rope Jumping Techniques (RJTs).

participant to adjust gradually to the demands of rope jumping rather than forcing them to adapt immediately.

LITs are rarely given up completely, however, because they add another dimension of fun and variety to rope jumping. If traditional programs offer hundreds of ways to jump over a rope, then LITs add hundreds of ways to whirl, wrap, step through, and catch a rope. For advanced rope artists, LITs even make it easier to incorporate other disciplines such as dance, gymnastics, and the martial arts. The routines in rhythmic gymnastics, a growing women's Olympic sport, incorporate LITs for just the same reason.

Traditional Complaint #3: Rope Jumping Is Boring

Adults and teenagers voice complaint #3 more often than children. Apparently, at some time during adolescence, people decide that they are less interested in jump rope games, rhymes, and variations like Double Dutch. Instead, they become more intrigued by variations and goals not offered by traditional rope jumping.

With respect to goals, traditional adult rope jumpers tended to strive for either speed (jump as fast as possible for a certain length of time) or endurance (jump for a certain period of time or for as long as possible). While these goals are certainly admirable and even recognized by *The Guinness Book of World Records*, they don't light everyone's fire. One can argue that getting in shape is enough of a goal. But then why do we have 10-kilometer runs, keep score in a tennis match, and prefer exercise machines that track our progress with electronic digital readouts?

As mentioned earlier, hundreds of jump rope techniques exist. Unfortunately, however, most people cannot experience this variety for the reasons already listed: The tricks that could add variety are too difficult to learn without instruction and too physically demanding for beginners. The latter problem is made worse by the fact that doing tricks usually increases the energy demands of rope jumping. For example, the Front Cross (page 107) increases the energy cost by 30%.

Ropics' Answer to Complaint #3: Organize Rope Jumping's Techniques to Guide and Motivate

With the strategies already outlined, the solution to complaint #3 is close at hand. We know that anyone can learn a vast number of techniques (also called *tricks*) with step-by-step instruction. In fact, watching our students learn techniques three times faster than I did is a source of pride and mild irritation for me. Also, my students don't become exhausted while doing the more demanding techniques like Front Crosses because they simply add more Low-Impact Techniques to lower the intensity. Now, for the other part of the solution.

Mastering the countless jump rope techniques can provide motivating goals as well as immense variety. Since techniques can vary greatly in degree of difficulty, however, you must be certain to learn the more basic techniques before you try the advanced; otherwise, you can become bewildered and frustrated rather than motivated. The Ropics program provides long-term goals and the guidance you need by dividing techniques into five levels of difficulty. Level 1 techniques are the easiest whereas Level 5 is the most difficult. In regard to dividing the techniques into levels, Ropics is much like the belt system used in karate and other martial arts. You want to feel confident about Level 1 techniques before setting your sights on Level 2.

To give you an even better idea of how challenging a technique is, Ropics assigns a difficulty factor (DF) to each technique. A Windmill, which is the most basic technique, has a DF of 1.0. The Jogging Step, a more difficult Level 1 technique, has a DF of 1.8. Level 2 techniques have DFs of 2.0 to 2.9. Level 3 techniques have DFs of 3.0 to 3.9, and so on. Difficulty factors increase guidance and let you set short-term goals of mastering slightly more challenging individual techniques.

Table 2.1 illustrates how Ropics divides techniques according to level of difficulty. As you can see, both Rope Jumping Techniques (RJTs) and LITs range from Level 1 to Level 5 in difficulty.

Table 2.1   **Ropics Short Rope Technique Organization**

Technique divisions	Skill levels				
	Level 1[a]	Level 2[b]	Level 3[c]	Level 4[d]	Level 5[e]
Rope Jumping Techniques	Two-Foot Jump	Scissors	Double Unders	Triple Unders	Quadruple Unders
Low-Impact Techniques	Windmills	Waist Wrap	Open Layout	Double Toss	Spin Kick Step-Through

Note. The techniques listed represent only one of many techniques in each level.
[a]Beginning. [b]Intermediate. [c]Advanced intermediate. [d]Advanced. [e]Master.

Wrap-Up

As will be more apparent when you read the next chapter, rope jumping *is* an excellent way to become fit. All the pluses of rope jumping are of little use, however, if people find it nonmotivating, frustrating to learn, or too strenuous to do. The Ropics program removes these minuses with tried-and-true strategies based on science and extensive experience. As you'll also see in chapter 3, Ropics also improves upon rope jumping's many pluses.

CHAPTER 3

How Ropics Can Improve Your Fitness

Aerobic dance, power walking, circuit training, and *triathlons* are all words that have been added to our fitness vocabulary over the past few years. Nevertheless, nothing surpasses the jump rope for developing cardiovascular fitness, burning calories, improving muscular tone, promoting self-esteem, providing fun and variety. . . . But, rather than list the 20 benefits and advantages of Ropics right here, I'll delve further into how this program can do so many things for you.

Develops Health-Related Fitness in Five Ways

Physical fitness is not an all-or-nothing phenomenon. Rather, it is a spectrum of different qualities that have varying degrees of influence on our health and how well we deal with the physical demands of our world. *Total fitness* refers to the ideal where each of these qualities is developed to its full potential. As the following list of benefits illustrates, no other single exercise allows you to approach that ideal better than Ropics.

Areas of Health-Related Fitness Promoted by Ropics

- Improves cardiovascular fitness.
- Promotes leanness (burns calories).
- Increases muscle tone and muscular endurance.
- Builds strong bones.
- Provides stretching exercises to improve flexibility.

Cardiovascular Fitness (or Aerobic Conditioning)

As I have noted, regular exercise is critical for long-term well-being. Research indicates that one class of exercise is especially good at reversing the consequences of inactivity such as heart disease and high blood pressure. In the late 1960s, Dr. Kenneth Cooper proposed a catchy adjective for this beneficial class of exercise: *aerobic*. Dr. Cooper defines *aerobic exercise* as "those activities that require oxygen for prolonged periods and place such demands on the body that it is required to improve its capacity to handle oxygen." Let me further explain this two-part definition.

The first half of Dr. Cooper's definition states that for an exercise to be *aerobic*, you must do it *continuously* for more than a short period of time. Therefore, sports like power lifting, baseball, gymnastics, and the 100-yard dash—which have brief, intermittent periods of activity—do not qualify as aerobic.

How long must you do an activity before it is considered aerobic? That depends on the second and most important part of the definition.

The second qualification for aerobic exercise is that it must improve the body's ability to use oxygen. The body can improve its ability to use oxygen by increasing effective lung capacity, developing a stronger heart, increasing blood volume, and improving the skeletal muscles' efficiency at "converting" oxygen to energy. These changes are referred to as improved cardiovascular fitness or aerobic conditioning. Although video games, bowling, and Christmas shopping can be done for extended periods of time, they fail to qualify because they don't improve cardiovascular fitness. Exercises that do improve cardiovascular fitness require repetitive and rhythmic use of large muscle groups for *at least 20 minutes at a time*. Familiar examples of qualified aerobic exercises include bicycling, distance running, cross-country skiing, walking, swimming, aerobic dance, and, of course, rope jumping.

Let's see how rope jumping qualifies as an aerobic exercise. First, although you might have some doubts, most people are able to jump rope for at least 20 minutes at a time after they have practiced a few weeks. With personal coaching, beginners can usually jump rope for 10 to 15 minutes on the first day. (The program in this book begins more conservatively because an experienced instructor isn't there to guide you.) The second qualification is also met because the large muscles of the legs are repetitively and rhythmically used for jumping while the arm and shoulder muscles are continuously used for turning the rope. Finally, and most conclusively, several scientific studies have proved that rope jumping does enhance cardiovascular fitness.

The ability of rope jumping to enhance cardiovascular fitness doesn't just improve your long-term health. Within weeks, you will also have the endurance to dash up a flight of stairs without becoming winded, the energy to go out dancing on Saturday night again, and that head of steam you need to feel good at the end of a long workday.

Leanness (or Burns Calories)

Aerobic exercise has other benefits besides developing cardiovascular fitness. It's also great at burning calories. America is obsessed with getting rid of calories and hence excess fat. Despite the constant deluge of "miracle" diets, pills, and weight loss methods, 35% of Americans are still overweight, and the statistics show no sign of improving. Alarmingly, a 1987 study by Dr. S.L. Gortmaker and his colleagues showed that the prevalence of obesity among children has increased over the last 20 years anywhere from 17% to 300% depending on the group studied!

Along with all the social disadvantages, obesity also has its own health risks: Diabetes, back strains, gallstones, high blood pressure, arthritis, and complications of pregnancy are just a few of the problems that become more common with obesity. The risk for heart disease also indirectly increases.

It is tempting to say that we should eat less. On the average, however, we Americans actually consume fewer calories than we did 90 years ago when we were more svelte. One reason we continue to gain weight may be that we have increased the fat in our diet by 30%. The probable major contributor, however, is that our activity level has decreased dramatically. Motorized transportation, electronic entertainment, and workplace automation have whittled away the opportunities for movement to the point that we are now 75% less active than in the year 1900. Regular aerobic exercise like Ropics provides the perfect opportunity to get the body moving again and burn those calories that used to be shed churning butter, splitting logs, or scrubbing clothes.

Rope jumping at a casual rate burns between 150 and 200 calories every 15 minutes for an average-size adult. Speed jumping or doing "tricks" increase the calorie-burning rate further, whereas Low-Impact Techniques (LITs) decrease the rate. Table 3.1 can give you a more accurate estimation of how many calories you would burn given your weight. When you realize that you must burn 3,500 calories to get rid of 1 pound of fat, you might get discouraged and sit down and have a piece of apple pie (about 300 calories). Realize, however, that excess fat doesn't appear over-

Table 3.1   **Estimation of Calories Burned While Jumping Rope**

Body weight (pounds)	Calories per minute
100	8.6
105	9.0
110	9.5
115	9.9
120	10.3
125	10.7
130	11.2
135	11.6 Example:
	11.6 × 15 minutes = 174 calories
140	12.0
145	12.4
150	12.9
155	13.4
160	13.8
165	14.2
170	14.7
175	15.1
180	15.5
185	15.9
190	16.4
195	16.8
200	17.2
205	17.7
210	18.1
215	18.5
220	18.9
225	19.4

To estimate how many calories you burned during a workout session, first find your body weight in column 1. Now multiply the adjacent number in column 2 by the number of minutes you jumped rope. The result is your caloric expenditure. The example shows the calculation for a 135-pound person who jumped for 15 minutes.

night. Rather, we accumulate fat gradually over weeks, months, and even years. Taking the weight off safely requires a similar amount of time and a real commitment to regular exercise. Proper diet and counseling can also be important, so you should see a registered dietician or join a reputable weight loss organization if you have a serious weight problem.

Of course, prevention is immeasurably better than cure. Over 90% of overweight children will remain overweight as adults, and over 90% of adults who lose weight from a diet gain it back in a year or two. Regular exercise can help prevent a child, or adult, from becoming overweight; this is by far the best strategy.

Muscular Endurance and Tone

If the body's rule for fat is Use it to lose it, then the opposite applies to muscles: Use it *or* lose it. These rules seem downright unfair, until you understand that the body's primary priority is to conserve rather than spend energy. After all, famine has been exceedingly more common throughout human history than abundance. Fat is the body's most efficient way to conserve energy, but the body must spend energy to build and maintain muscles and bones. Therefore, the body tries to get by with as little muscle as necessary to survive. As the body's reasoning goes, if you don't use them, you don't need them. You need only witness the leg size of a wheelchair-restricted person to appreciate how far muscles can shrink, or atrophy, when not put to use.

One of the strengths of Ropics is the number of muscle groups it uses. As I have mentioned, rope jumpers use the various muscles of the legs and buttocks for jumping, while they use the muscles of the forearms, upper arms, and shoulders for gripping, turning, and controlling the rope. Rope jumpers who do tricks use even more muscles. For example, Front Crosses (see page 107) recruit the chest and upper back muscles. Side Straddles (page 101) require the use of the leg abductors and adductors, whereas Step-Throughs (pages 98-99) employ the hip flexors.

Admittedly, practicing Ropics won't build as much strength or bulk as lifting a set of weights, but it will give your many muscles the endurance they need to meet life's everyday challenges, like bounding up stairs and carrying bags of groceries. For the socially self-conscious, Ropics will also give your muscles that tone and firmness they need to help you look your best.

Strong Bones

Speaking of looking your best, don't forget about your skeletal system, the frame on which your muscles and other tissues depend. Exercises like rope jumping have repeatedly been shown to be an important hedge against developing osteoporosis, a painful and disfiguring malady of old age. Also known as *brittle bones*, osteoporosis affects about 24 million Americans and threatens to become an even bigger problem as our population ages. Osteoporosis occurs when the bones do not contain enough calcium to make them strong. When you see elderly people with humped backs, they probably endure collapsed vertebrae from osteoporosis. If you hear that someone's aunt just broke her hip, chances are that osteoporosis was a major factor.

To understand how exercise helps prevent osteoporosis, remember the Use it or lose it rule. When you exercise, you stress the bones as well as the muscles. Your body senses this stress and sends more calcium (if available) and other needed nutrients into the bones to make them stronger. If you decide instead of exercising to watch a TV show, your body receives one more signal verifying that you don't really need those strong bones. Then, as you age, your weakening bones will be less able to manage the minor stresses of everyday living.

Of course, the cause of osteoporosis is usually more complicated than not enough exercise. In this age of "junk food," researchers believe that calcium deficiency also plays an important role. According to the National Academy of Science, young people need about 1,200 mg of calcium per day (the equivalent of four glasses of milk) to build a "bank" of strong bones. Adults and the elderly need at least 800 mg of calcium per day. Vitamin D deficiency, heredity, hormones, smoking, and gender are other factors that play important roles.

The typical profile of a person at great risk for osteoporosis would be a small-framed, postmenopausal woman who smokes and thrives on junk food while avoiding dairy products and exercise. Nevertheless, osteoporosis can strike anyone, and research has shown that exercise with proper diet does make the bones stronger, whereas calcium pills *alone* do not.

Flexibility

One other facet of physical fitness directly affects your health—flexibility. Flexibility depends on long, supple muscles and tendons around the body's many joints. These tissues, and not the joints themselves, allow a gymnast to do the splits with such ease, while most of us might more literally split if we tried such a stunt.

As you might guess, people who have stiff muscles are at greater risk for tearing muscles than those who are flexible. Muscle tears, more commonly known as strains, can occur with any sudden movement or even minor stress. Hamstring, groin, and calf strains are just a few of the more common muscle injuries. The most notorious of all muscle strains, however, is the lower back strain, also referred to as a *back pull*, a *back kink*, or even *throwing the back out*. Each year, millions of people, seeking relief from the excruciating pain of back strains, lose hundreds of dollars from time absent from work and from doctor and chiropractor bills. Obesity, weak back and abdominal muscles, and inflexible hamstring muscles contribute to this painful but common condition.

As with strength, firmness, and size, muscles can be trained to become more flexible. Unfortunately, aerobic exercise, including rope jumping, develops only a limited degree of flexibility. Therefore, Ropics includes safe stretching exercises like those illustrated on pages 66-70. But the flexibility gained through stretching can be put to use with the jump rope with techniques like the Leg Over Pass (page 90), Knee Lifts (page 106), and Open Layout (page 113).

Improves Six Areas of Lifestyle-Related Fitness

The other areas of fitness that Ropics develops have little, if any, direct influence on health. They do, however, help us deal with the many little challenges that the world throws our way, such as traversing a toy-strewn floor, catching a toppling vase, or learning a new dance step. Competitive athletes are especially concerned about these other areas of fitness, because they affect their performance. It's no surprise then that football, basketball, and tennis players, wrestlers, and, of course, boxers all jump rope to help round out their training programs.

One word of assurance—as you review the various areas that Ropics develops, don't be concerned about mastering new coordination, timing, rhythm, and the rest all at once. As I discussed in chapter 2, the Ropics program teaches each technique step-by-step to avoid such intimidating situations.

Furthermore, you will acquire many of these qualities without trying. In many ways, the jump rope turns out to be a rather subtle coach.

Areas of Lifestyle-Related Fitness Promoted by Ropics
- Improves coordination.
- Enhances agility.
- Improves timing.
- Improves rhythm.
- Increases kinesthetic awareness.
- Enhances quickness.

Coordination

Coordination, or the ability to execute a chosen movement precisely, is a quality that few of us believe we have developed. Most of us readily consign ourselves to being full-fledged members of the "Klutz Corps" without ever seeking a transfer. Eddie Race, a dynamic senior rope jumper and friend of mine, has convincingly proved that transfers from the corps can be made.

Eddie was a counselor at a high school and jumped rope regularly every noon. One day Bill, a special education student, who expressed hesitant interest in learning how to jump rope, approached Eddie. Bill's reluctance was understandable. After all, besides being "special," he was 6 feet 4 inches tall and weighed 295 pounds. Bill's progress was slow at first. Like many special-education children, he had been denied many opportunities for developing his coordination because he had been shunned or picked last for games, sports, and other activities. Furthermore, by high school he had gotten the message that he was "slow," which didn't help his confidence. Regardless, after practicing a few weeks, he sported a grin that stretched from ear to ear as he flawlessly performed rope techniques at speeds that would have made a boxer proud. (Over a year, he also lost 100 pounds.)

Drawn by the fun and challenge, other special-education children soon joined Eddie and Bill for their noon workouts and challenged each other with speed-jumping drills and technique mastery. As their coordination and general fitness improved, so did their confidence—especially when they began receiving requests for demonstrations at school assemblies, club meetings, and other events.

Among other things, Eddie Race proved that even though we are born with varying degrees of coordination, we have the ability to improve our coordination immensely if given the chance. All we need is a little confidence, proper instruction, and practice.

The Rope Jumping and Low-Impact Techniques of Ropics are effective methods to develop coordination, because even basic skills require a harmony of movement among the legs, the arms, and the rope. If the harmony isn't there, the rope will remind you until you get it. Once you have mastered the basics (and you will), you will have literally thousands of other techniques to choose from so that you can continue to improve your coordination. Think of Ropics as a virtual smorgasbord for your coordination center and a one-way transfer out of the Klutz Corps.

Agility

Names like Fred Astaire, Dorothy Hamill, and Walter Payton all evoke images of effortless agility. What these artists and athletes share is an uncommon degree of balance, coordination, and quickness that allows them to move deftly about their chosen arena. Rope jumping can develop these qualities as effectively as running through any pattern of tires or reviewing any drill in tap dance. Unlike running through tires, rope jumping offers you innumerable ways to challenge and enhance your agility. If improving your agility is important, footwork techniques will be especially useful.

Timing

Timing is the ability to move at precisely the right moment. Timing is important for throwing a ball to your downfield receiver or throwing a punch while sparring in a boxing match. Rope jumping can enhance a sense of timing because so many techniques rely on this quality for successful completion. For example, Side Straddles, also known as jumping jacks, are a familiar exercise from calisthenics. Side Straddles with the rope require more exact timing than the exercise, however, since the feet must be apart only when the rope is overhead. Other more advanced techniques may require even more exact timing, so you can hone this quality as your needs require.

Rhythm

The ability to do a recurrent movement regularly in time is referred to as *rhythm*. For many Rope Jumping Techniques, the challenge lies not in acquiring a new level of coordination, agility, or timing, but in learning a new rhythm. For instance, the skills needed to do a Two-Foot Jump (pages 81-84) and a Double Under (page 115) are exactly the same except that each requires a different rhythm. With the Two-Foot Jump, the rope turns *once* for every jump; with the Double Under, the rope turns *twice* for each jump. The rhythm variations don't stop there!

Kinesthetic Awareness

There's a good chance that you've never heard about this less-celebrated area of fitness, even though you do possess it. Kinesthetic awareness refers to your ability to sense where and how your body parts are moving and positioned in space without looking. You use this sense whenever you reach for the light switch in the dark and even when you walk without looking at your feet. Dancers have especially keen kinesthetic awareness—they must know exactly how their heads, hands, legs, elbows, and other body parts are moving and positioned throughout a precisely choreographed routine.

Like dance, only a few techniques with the jump rope require eye–hand or eye–foot coordination. Nearly all techniques depend on your ability to sense how your hands are positioned and turning the rope while your feet do their job. Furthermore, advanced jump rope enthusiasts strive to learn techniques from every possible direction. The body must then also learn where the rope is in space. Thus, kinesthetic awareness can become yet another strong quality of an experienced jump rope enthusiast.

Quickness

In many sports, quickness is valued more highly than strength. After all, all the muscles of a champion bodybuilder won't do you much good if you swing the bat after the ball hits the catcher's glove or the football receiver you're supposed to be covering repeatedly feints and scampers down the field without you. Even situations that seem to rely on strength, such as throwing a shot put, often depend more on *power*, which is a product of strength *and* speed.

Whereas all the other areas of fitness mentioned are essentially automatically developed in Ropics, quickness is an option. Once you have mastered the basics, you can turn the rope at a casual rate or at lightning-like speed. Because Rope Jumping Techniques offer a wide variety of movements, you can tailor your speed drills to meet your needs. Need fast feet? Practice fast footwork techniques like the Cross Step (page 106). Need quick hands? Work on doing quick Front Crosses or Figure-Eights (pages 107 and 88, respectively). Need to change directions rapidly? Practice rapid 180-Degree Turn-Abouts (page 114).

Promotes Emotional Fitness in Four Ways

It's often difficult to sell young people on the health benefits of exercise, because they believe that they are immune to many of the sedentary diseases, which might not strike until age 50 or later.

Today's youth, as well as adults, can relate to emotional problems like stress, anxiety, depression, and low self-esteem—all of which are favorably affected by regular exercise.

Areas of Emotional Fitness Promoted by Ropics

- Relieves stress.
- Reduces anxiety and depression.
- Improves self-esteem.
- Enhances sexuality.

Relieves Stress

Along with the decrease in physical demands brought about by technology comes an increase in emotional demands or stress. Common experience and research indicate that exercise is a remarkably effective way to alleviate stress. How an exercise program like Ropics reduces stress is not exactly known, but it probably involves several mechanisms. One likely mechanism is diversion. For example, concentrating on what technique you're going to try next diverts your attention so that you don't fume about the impossible assignment your boss just gave you.

Exercise might also calm you by inducing the release of endorphins in the brain. These powerful hormones seem to be the body's own brand of painkiller and tranquilizer. The release of endorphins into the bloodstream is probably the cause of the frequently reported "runner's high," which I've experienced with rope jumping as well as running. Admittedly, the role of endorphins in stress reduction is still controversial, although tantalizing.

Another hormone that plays a more definite role in stress is adrenalin. Among many other things, adrenalin elevates heart rate and blood pressure, increases strength, dilates the pupils, and slows digestion. All these changes prepare us for the "fight or flight" response, which was appropriate for our ancestors when they faced a hungry tiger or a hostile tribe. These changes don't fit the more typical challenges of our modern world, such as dealing with a difficult customer or loosening a stubborn bolt. In most circles it's not socially acceptable to punch someone in the face or run screaming down the hall. Ropics, on the other hand, is socially acceptable and allows your body to do what the adrenalin has been urging it to do all the frustrating, nerve-racking, day long—move!

Finally, and perhaps most importantly, lack of exercise is stressful in itself because our bodies are designed for physical activity. Through the ages, the human race has had to chase down food, wrestle with enemies, run after each other, and just plain move. Our technological society has eliminated many opportunities to move, and our bodies don't like the inactivity. And if your body doesn't like all the rest it's getting, you can be sure that it's complaining to the brain whether you realize it or not. If you have any doubts, try staying in bed for several days or watch a caged animal; restlessness is inevitable.

Reduces Anxiety and Depression

Stress can do more harm than make us feel upset or restless. It also contributes to anxiety and depression—two emotional disorders that frequently occur together. We can easily understand how someone can become anxious with all the conflicts that usually surround stress and the effects of adrenalin on the body and mind. We might, however, have difficulty with understanding how stress can lead to depression. The concept is easier to grasp if we view it as emotional surrender to conflict.

If exercise like rope jumping reduces stress, then it might also reduce the likelihood of anxiety and depression. Research supports this line of reasoning. People who exercise are less often depressed or anxious than those who are sedentary. Furthermore, exercise can often help those who are already depressed.

Improves Self-Esteem

Having low self-esteem, or a poor estimation of oneself, is also a frequent contributor to depression and anxiety. For a number of good reasons, Ropics is particularly well suited for raising one's self-esteem. For one, it includes many reachable goals, which can give you that extra measure of self-confidence that springs from achievement. It also doesn't hurt to look in a mirror and see your muscles turn firmer, your abdomen become slimmer, your feet more nimble, and all the other good things that can happen to your body.

The comments we receive from our peers affect our self-esteem more powerfully than even a mirror. Currently, rope jumping is generally viewed as an activity that requires great stamina and coordination. Therefore, others automatically deem anyone who can do basic rope jumping to be in good shape. If you learn to do a few tricks with the jump rope, you become a certified athlete in the minds of others. My own personal experience confirms this claim. From grade school through college, my classmates knew me for my academic rather than my athletic abilities, and I was frequently picked near last for team sports. When I was a junior in college I began jumping rope. By the time I reached medical school, I was skilled enough to do demonstrations. I was still pleasantly taken aback, however, when another student mentioned that I was considered "the athlete" of the medical school class. This revelation surprised me since our class had more than one or two former college football, track, and wrestling stars.

If verbal praise doesn't raise your self-esteem, then applause might do the trick. The sight of a rope whirling in synchrony with the arms and feet attracts admiring onlookers at any gym or health club. Add a few dexterous techniques, and you just might be overwhelmed by requests for demonstrations!

Enhances Sexuality

Perhaps I should mention one more benefit of Ropics—improved sexuality. Studies have thoroughly documented that people who exercise regularly both enjoy sex more and have more sex. It's just another consequence of the body being tuned up. Ropics is a great way to keep the "spark" going or perhaps to get it back.

Provides Five Other Advantages

As you can see, Ropics has much to offer the mind as well as the body. All these benefits would be out of reach for many, however, if it drained the pocketbook, required Mediterranean-like weather, or was numbingly boring. Fortunately for us, that's not the case.

Additional Advantages of Ropics

- It's inexpensive.
- It's portable.
- It's not dependent on special facilities or weather conditions.
- It's safe.
- It's fun!

Inexpensive

Many people hesitate to buy a quality exercise machine. After all, purchasing some of this equipment can wipe out a checking account, and our interest in this machinery often wanes before the warranties expire. A quality jump rope, on the other hand, can cost less than $10 and has more variety built into it than *any* chrome-laden electronic machine. The most costly item needed for rope jumping is a good pair of aerobic dance or cross-training shoes ($40–$80). The rest of the needed apparel is probably already hanging in your closet or locker. (For more information on shoes and apparel, see chapter 5.)

Portable

Many people in our on-the-go society live out of a suitcase. Fortunately, a jump rope fits handily in a suitcase or a briefcase, so you can take this all-purpose exercise "machine" with you anywhere.

Not Dependent on Special Facilities or Weather Conditions

Swimming, racket sports, and cross-country skiing are all excellent aerobic activities, but they require facilities that aren't always handy or particular weather conditions. For Ropics, all you need is enough room to swing the rope and a smooth, even floor surface to jump on. Gymnasiums, racquetball courts, weight rooms, and exercise studios will do if the weather is foul. If fair weather is beckoning you to come outdoors, wood decks, pool sides, and tennis or basketball courts will do. (For more information on floor surfaces, see chapter 5.)

Safe

How safe an activity is depends on many factors. Some activities such as running and bicycling pose the greatest risk of major injury due to the environment in which they are often practiced—the streets. The very nature of other activities poses risk of injury. Paralysis and death still occur in football due to neck injuries from errant blocks and tackles. With swimming, drowning is always a possibility, especially in natural bodies of water.

Admittedly, no activity, including rope jumping, is without some risk. The benefits of a prudent exercise program will, however, far outweigh the risks of being inactive. Instructors and program developers have the job of making the benefits outweigh the risks by as much as possible. With rope jumping, we already have a good head start. There is little or no chance of collision with other participants or sudden unexpected moves to place the bones and muscles at risk. Territorial dogs and inattentive car drivers shouldn't be a problem unless you decide to skip down the street. As discussed in chapter 2, Ropics also minimizes the risk of the more minor overuse injuries such as shin splints by giving careful instruction, a graduated program, and recommendations on proper equipment.

Fun!

Of course, even the best exercise program in blueprint is worthless if it doesn't generate smiles. In this regard, Ropics is unsurpassed. Children all over the world already spend entire recesses playing with the jump rope. For people of all age groups, boredom plagues only the uninformed; you can learn thousands of techniques and include them in your workouts. Some people also enjoy endurance or speed jumping. For those who prefer to exercise alone, it's nearly always possible to find a vacant room or gym corner. Those who thrive on comaraderie can gather fellow enthusiasts for a stimulating class.

Finally, and perhaps most importantly, rope jumping and music are natural partners. Not only does a strong beat provide the tempo for turning the rope and moving the feet, but the changing rhythms and melodies also give the impetus for varying techniques and style. To be honest, I got hooked on this side of rope jumping more than any other. If desired, you can also aspire to become a rope artist—an enthusiast who views the rope not as a piece of exercise equipment, but as a versatile, expressive extension of self.

Wrap-Up

Few, if any, exercise programs can measure up to the effectiveness, versatility, and accessibility of Ropics. Your ability to develop nearly every major area of fitness with Ropics makes it attractive for anyone who is looking for an efficient all-around exercise. Because Ropics is inexpensive, portable, and independent of weather conditions and special facilities, it won't stress your lifestyle or wallet. With an open mind, a little instruction, and motivating music, people of all age groups and fitness levels and both sexes can rediscover the fun just waiting to be tapped from their old grade-school friend—the jump rope. Table 3.2 compares Ropics to other popular aerobic activities in terms of those qualities people look for in an exercise program.

Table 3.2 Comparison of Qualities Affecting Effectiveness and Accessibility of Popular Exercises*

	Ropics	Walking/ running	Biking	Aerobic dance	Swimming	Cross-country skiing	Racket sports (singles)
Cardiovascular fitness	1	1	1	1	1	1	2
Muscular endurance (upper body: lower body)	1:1	3:1	3:1	2:1	1:1	1:1	2:2
Calorie burning	1	1	1	1	3	1	2
Motor skills (e.g., timing, coordination)	1	4	4	1	2-3	3	2

Inexpense	1	3	1	1-2	2-3	1-3
Portability	1	3	1	1	3	2
Weather independence	2-3	3	1	1-3	3-4	1-3
Availability of facilities	1	1-3	1	2-4	3-4	3
Variety of movement	4	4	1	3	3	2

*1 = Excellent, 2 = good, 3 = fair, 4 = poor

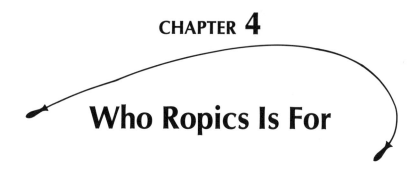

CHAPTER **4**

Who Ropics Is For

As is evident from the long list of benefits, nearly anyone can profit from Ropics including men and women, young and old, and world-class athletes or novice fitness enthusiasts. Before I outline what Ropics can do for you, you should determine whether you should visit a doctor before exercising.

Does Physical Condition Matter?

Beginning a regular program of exercise is one of the most positive steps you can make toward your long-term well-being. Exercise does, however, pose new demands on your body. Therefore, you should see your doctor for a checkup if you are over 35 years old and have not been active or are over 40 years of age. You should get clearance from your doctor regardless of age if you have any of the following health concerns or risk factors:

- Heart or lung disease
- Diabetes
- Arthritis
- Sickle cell disease
- Pregnancy
- High blood pressure
- Smoking history
- High cholesterol or lipid blood levels
- Family history of heart disease

Exercise in itself does not cause heart attacks unless you already have a badly diseased heart. Some people, however, do not know that their heart is in a precarious state of health, as is sadly exemplified by the late Jim Fixx, the running guru who ignored his own advice that anyone with risk factors for heart disease should get a checkup.

You should also put exercise on hold if you are fighting an acute illness such as the common cold, influenza, or stomach flu. Wait until the fever and severe symptoms pass. Your body is already stressed enough trying to fight the bug.

Although certain physical conditions may make exercising with the jump rope inadvisable, age itself does not. Ropics has something for all age groups.

Does Age Matter?

Ropics is an appropriate activity for participants no matter what their age. Children, young adults, middle-aged people, and older adults can all glean benefits from a regular exercise program.

Children

Despite the strides made in adult fitness, many people and organizations believe that our children are in the worst physical shape ever. For evidence, they point to our children's rising rate of obesity, diminishing scores on fitness tests, and increasing time spent in front of the TV. It's tempting to say that our schools should do a better job with physical education and that the toy industry should develop more toys and games powered by muscles rather than by batteries. However, as with discipline, nutrition, and other important qualities, fitness should begin at home.

You could take a number of strategies to promote your child's fitness such as limiting TV time or encouraging healthy activities like soccer, bicycling, and swimming. Ropics is another good option, of course, and it also presents at least one other strategy: Exercise with your children.

Ropics is one of the few aerobic exercise programs that allows the family to work out effectively together. Even though jogging, biking, or swimming together is certainly beneficial, you might not feel like you're getting a good workout as your youngster struggles to keep up. Aerobic dance, a stationary exercise that is popular with adults, hasn't seemed to have caught on with kids. Ropics, however, can be both challenging and enjoyable for you and your child.

Children enjoy rope jumping because they think of it as something much more important than exercise. They consider it to be play. Any attempt to sell Ropics to children as a great way to stay fit is likely to be met with failure because children really aren't interested in or don't understand how doing exercise today will prevent them from having a heart attack 40 years from now. Because children want to have fun, Ropics youth classes include many jump rope games in addition to the standard warm-up through cool-down phases. These classes focus on fun and play, but the result is the same as exercising: improved cardiovascular fitness, agility, quickness, coordination, self-confidence, and so on.

You can also incorporate games (and music) into Ropics workouts when your child or children join you. The appendix lists two books that describe a wide variety of challenging games for different age groups. Who knows, you might choose to include some of the games in your workouts even if no children are present!

Adult Men and Women

In contrast to children, the main challenge with encouraging adults to try rope jumping is simply convincing them that they *can* master the rope. Many have tried once or twice as an adult only to experience the problems discussed in chapter 2. Our adult students have proved that with proper instruction, they master the rope just as quickly as children. In fact, our men and women can do tricks that their kids haven't figured out how to do. The main difference between the two age groups is that unguided children simply don't give up as easily and are unafraid to try even the most challenging technique.

Rope jumping wasn't always recommended for women. During the 1800s, someone wrote that women foolish enough to jump rope would "pop" their blood vessels. Such nonsense was happily laid to rest during the 20th century when women athletes began surpassing the physical feats of their naive 19th century male counterparts. Of course, men and women can equally reap the benefits of Ropics listed in chapter 2 and have fun doing it. Men and women usually do want something a little different from exercise, however, especially in regard to enhancing their appearance. Men tend to want exercises that develop the muscles of the upper body to give them the classic V physique. Ropics is great for toning and defining the upper body because the arm, shoulder, chest, and upper back muscles power the whirling rope. Women, on the other hand, are more concerned with the shape of the calves, thighs, and buttocks. Again, Ropics can help since these muscle groups are used for jumping over the rope or marching in place while doing Low-Impact Techniques.

Middle Age and Beyond

Ponce de León labored through the swamps of Florida looking in vain for the Fountain of Youth. Unknown to the Spanish explorer, the very exercise he got looking for the fountain took him as close to eternal youth as he was going to get. Scientific research has shown that much of the physical deterioration that we attribute to age is due more to inactivity. For example, strength in adults who exercise regularly does not significantly decline until age 65, whereas those who are inactive begin to lose strength around 40 years of age. Those who exercise lose cardiovascular fitness half as fast as those who don't exercise; furthermore, active senior citizens may actually have faster reaction times than nonactive young adults!

Exercise programs like Ropics don't just slow the ravages of time; they can reverse them. Even people who are over 80 years old can become stronger, quicker, more flexible, and more cardiovascularly fit than they were, say, 10 years ago. The elderly need closer supervision as they work through an exercise program, but the effort benefits the participants. Exercise can mean the difference between being a bed-ridden nursing home resident and being an on-the-go senior citizen who looks and acts years younger than the birth certificate states.

Of course, even though our bodies respond well to exercise regardless of age, the body does respond more slowly as we grow older. Therefore, the Ropics program progresses its workouts more slowly for the older age groups. The endpoint is nevertheless the same. As I already noted, you should get a physician's okay before beginning any exercise program, just to be sure your body is ready for a little work. You will also want to ask your doctor if it's all right to engage in a moderate impact-type of exercise. The Ropics program is more forgiving to joints than activities like running and even traditional rope jumping, but some forms of arthritis and other physical conditions may require alternative forms of exercise.

Does Fitness Level Matter?

Whether you've just become interested in starting a fitness program or you've been an active athlete or exerciser for some time, Ropics can be adapted to your present level of fitness to ensure an effective workout.

Novice Fitness Enthusiasts

Sir Isaac Newton understood *inertia* first: "Whatever is at rest tends to stay at rest, and whatever is moving tends to keep moving." Inertia is your foe if you are trying to move a heavy rock, and it's also your foe if you are trying to get yourself to start an exercise program. Conversely, it's your friend once you've gotten yourself moving.

Even though your own willpower is required to overcome the inertia of rest, Ropics may require less willpower to get you moving than other activities. As I discussed earlier, it's not expensive, doesn't require California-like weather, and can be done alone or with a group. Also, if you follow the program, you should be able to avoid sore calves and shins. Many people who have purchased our Level 1 videotape became so excited about being able to jump rope that they would forget about our repeated warnings to include periods of Low-Impact Techniques in their workouts. Consequently, they would jump rope for 10 to 20 minutes straight on the first day and then hobble around on the second through fifth days.

There's still another fact that should help you get inertia on your side. People who are inactive will see greater changes in their level of fitness than those who are already active. For example, someone just starting a fitness program can increase his or her strength, cardiovascular fitness, flexibility, and agility by, say, 30% much more quickly and easily than a trained athlete could increase those qualities by the same percentage. Figure 4.1 shows why. As you become more fit, you must expend more time and effort to get further improvements. That's why Olympic athletes must train 8 hours a day to get that extra bit of improvement in performance, which can mean the difference between winning a gold medal and watching from the stands. Of course, becoming fit enough for your health and vitality doesn't require a substantial time commitment. With only one-half hour of Ropics, three times a week, your fitness won't be that far behind many full-time athletes.

If all the potential benefits and advantages of Ropics still don't push you off the couch, read chapter 6 for more tips on how to get and keep motivated.

Athletes or Those Who Are Already Active

Variety is the spice of life. That's just one reason why doing more than one type of exercise (or *cross-training*) has grown popular over the past few years. No matter how much you enjoy your favor-

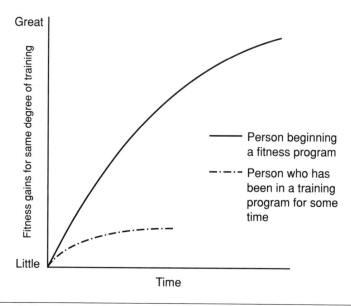

Figure 4.1   Those who are inactive can make faster gains in their fitness level than athletes who are already quite fit.

ite activity, you are sure to discover new joys in other programs like Ropics. Including Ropics with your other activities can also help you avoid the boredom of doing the same thing day after day. For example, Ropics is a natural complement to aerobic dance. They share similar movements, require the same facilities, and go superbly with music. In fact, you could look at Ropics as aerobic dance with a jump rope. Adding the jump rope, however, suddenly gives new life to familiar aerobic routines by providing different challenges, sensations, and objectives.

Cross-training with Ropics can complement your other activities in even more ways. It can develop those areas of fitness that less complete programs ignore. For example, Ropics can tone the upper body, enhance timing and coordination, and improve kinesthetic awareness—all qualities that are virtually untouched by running and bicycling. Swimming is a great all-around exercise, but perhaps you would like to burn more calories, for which Ropics is better. You might also choose Ropics to improve your agility for football, volleyball, racquetball, or whatever other sport you choose.

Doing more than one activity also has practical advantages. When the weather turns too nasty for outdoor activities, it's nice to be able to do something that is as much fun inside as it is outside. If you need to travel a great deal, it's good to have an exercise alternative that fits inside your suitcase and doesn't require a partner. If you can't buy downhill skis, boots, and lift tickets and also afford to join the indoor tennis club, Ropics offers you another option that costs peanuts and will keep you fit. Finally, the idea of cross-training is touted for its added safety. Doing the same exercise repeatedly may not only wear the mind, it can also wear on the same part of the body. Tendinitis, fasciitis, and other overuse injuries occur when repeated stresses break down tissues faster than the body can heal them. Different activities each tend to stress the body slightly differently so that overuse injuries become less likely.

Wrap-Up

To sum it up, Ropics just might be the spice you need to round out your fitness recipe whether you are young or mature, man or woman, out of shape or in top condition.

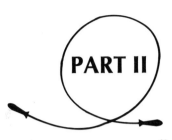

PART II

What You Need to Know to Begin Your Ropics Program

Now that you have a little background on Ropics and what it can do for you, it's time to get yourself ready for the Ropics workout. Chapter 5 gives you the information you need to know about selecting jump ropes, apparel, places to jump, and music. Since getting started and dropping out are common problems for even those with the best intentions, chapter 6 reviews some useful ways to get and keep yourself motivated for a lifetime commitment to exercise. Chapter 7 examines the different sections of a Ropics workout from warm-up to cool-down and discusses how each section is important for safely and effectively gaining fitness. You'll also learn how to avoid becoming overly fatigued or sore regardless of your current level of fitness. In short, Part II contains the information that is most important for you to know before you begin to exercise with a jump rope.

CHAPTER 5

Learning the Ropes and Other Information

As I've shown in the preceding chapters, Ropics has hefty credits on the balance sheet. In order to keep the balance in the black, it's essential that you use the proper jump ropes, apparel, shoes, and floor surface. The appropriate music further enhances Ropics' appeal.

Choosing the Right Jump Rope

Jump ropes are obviously central to Ropics, and their apparent simplicity is deceptive because their performance can be affected by their length, weight, aerodynamic drag, and ease in turning at the ends. At one time, your choice of jump ropes was limited to a #9 sash cord from the hardware store or a deluxe leather rope from the sporting goods store. Now, ropes are made from a dozen or more different materials and come in many different designs. Choosing the right one and making certain it is the correct length can mean the difference between immediate enjoyment and repeated frustration.

How to Measure a Jump Rope

A jump rope that is too short for you will lead to bad jumping posture and frequent misses, especially with fancy techniques. A rope that is too long will strike the floor in front of the feet and bounce up and hit the ankles. Figure 5.1 shows you how to measure a jump rope for your height. The end of the handles should just reach your armpits while you stand on the middle of the rope with one or two feet.

Figure 5.1   Measuring the correct jump rope length.

If the rope is too long, you will have to shorten it according to the instructions of that particular brand or style. You might be able to shorten a rope that isn't adjustable by tying one or more knots in the rope several inches from the end as in Figure 5.2. If the rope requires more than four knots, you should get a shorter rope. By the way, you can shorten segmented ropes, which are described later in the chapter, without unsightly knots to fit even the smallest jumper. Segmented ropes can also be tailor-made to fit tall people who cannot find any store models that fit them.

How to Choose a Jump Rope

Despite the many different choices of jump ropes available today, there are still some common qualities to look for when making a selection:

• Look for ropes that are well constructed and made of durable materials. Because ropes are generally inexpensive, just a couple of dollars often separates good, durable models from the cheap models that won't make it through a workout.

• The rope should turn easily within the handle, but bearings are not always necessary. Ropes that turn with a swivel are gener-

Figure 5.2   How to shorten a rope that is not adjustable.

ally prone to early wear. Speed and segmented ropes turn well inside the handles even without bearings.

• Avoid ropes that stretch to any significant degree when a section is pulled between your hands. Elasticlike jump ropes are unwieldy, especially at faster speeds.

• Make certain that the handles fit comfortably in your hands. Women and children may find some handles too large to be comfortable for extended periods of time. If you tend to get sweaty palms, it's nice if the handles have foam rubber grips.

Types of Jump Ropes

Although there are many different models of jump ropes, most fall into one of the categories discussed here. Each category has its own particular strengths and weaknesses. Since ropes usually cost less than $10 and don't take up much room, it won't stress your pocketbook or duffel bag to have more than one type of rope on hand to fit your different needs. For example, a segmented rope might be your favorite all-around rope. When trying to learn a difficult technique, however, you might keep handy a cotton rope, which doesn't sting when you miss. If you like to include bursts of speed jumping in your workout, you could throw a speed rope into your duffle bag. Let me review the choices.

Segmented Ropes (or Beaded Ropes)

Segmented ropes (see Figure 5.3) have short cylindrical plastic beads strung on an inner nylon cord. They are the best all-around rope for Ropics because they don't twist upon themselves as easily as other ropes do with Low-Impact Techniques. Due to the added weight of the beads, they are less affected by the wind if you like outdoor jumping and more forgiving to slight errors in technique execution. Since the inner nylon cord is quite flexible, they work the best for Low-Impact Techniques like whirls and wraps and form a nice arc to jump through even at slow turning speeds.

Beware of cheap, usually imported, segmented ropes that have brittle segments that break on impact with a hard floor. If made of quality materials, these ropes are durable although eventually the segments that strike the floor will wear out. If you purchase an extra segmented rope, you can make your primary rope last a *long* time by simply replacing the worn segments with new segments from your spare-parts rope. Finally, these ropes can be made to fit anyone's height. You can easily remove segments by untying the

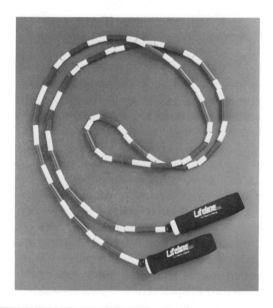

Figure 5.3 A segmented jump rope.

knot at one end of the nylon cord, which is found inside the handle. Therefore, you can shorten these ropes to fit even the most petite jumper. If you are too tall for any store model, you can buy a longer nylon cord from a hardware store and restring the segments.

As mentioned before, no rope is perfect. The main disadvantage to a segmented rope is that it stings the most when it strikes your body during a miss. Therefore, you should have one of the following types of ropes handy when learning a particularly challenging technique.

Cotton or Synthetic Woven Ropes

Jump ropes woven from materials like hemp and straw predate all other types. Woven ropes today are usually made from cotton, nylon, or polypropylene (see Figure 5.4). The principal advantage to a woven rope is that it stings the least (especially the cotton variety) when the rope accidentally strikes you. Therefore, some people keep a woven rope around in case they are having trouble mastering a difficult technique. If you plan to use a woven rope

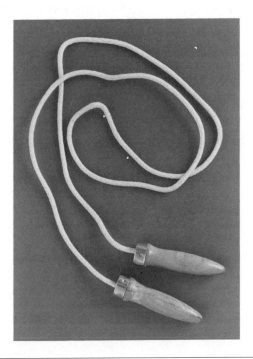

Figure 5.4   A cotton jump rope.

frequently, be sure that it has ball bearings at the ends for easy turning. The durability of woven ropes is good in general, although ropes made from polypropylene tend to fray and snag carpet fibers if you jump on this surface. Also, ropes that use swivels instead of bearings usually don't last long.

The same quality that makes woven ropes forgiving while learning difficult techniques also makes them less forgiving in other situations. Woven ropes have a relatively rough surface that gives them higher aerodynamic drag. Drag might seem like an insignificant issue until you realize that the middle of a rope can attain speeds of up to 65 miles per hour while speed jumping. Drag is a factor at even moderate speeds, however, and misses tend to be more frequent with woven ropes. The wind also likes to "grab" these ropes, which makes them difficult to control outdoors.

Speed Ropes (or Licorice Ropes)

Aptly named, speed ropes (Figure 5.5) are made from vinyl plastic cords that resemble a strand of licorice candy—their other namesake. These are the fastest type of rope because they are light and cut the air well. Speed ropes are also quite durable and inexpensive. Unfortunately, speed ropes tend to become gnarled during

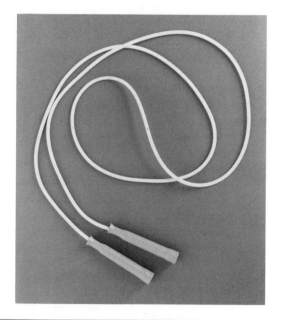

Figure 5.5   A speed (or licorice) rope.

some of the common Low-Impact Techniques. It's also easier to miss with them because their light weight makes them less forgiving to slight errors in technique execution. Like woven ropes, speed ropes usually need knots tied in the cord to be shortened.

Leather Ropes

Leather ropes (Figure 5.6) evoke images of sweaty boxing gyms and tough, intent pugilists. Because leather ropes have been associated with athletes and the other ropes have been found mainly on playgrounds, some people still consider the leather rope the only serious jump rope on the market. In fact, however, even though leather ropes are good for traditional rope jumping, they have no significant advantage over speed ropes. Like speed ropes, they are fast, but they are more expensive and less durable. They also tend to become gnarled with some Low-Impact Techniques.

Weighted Ropes

You should consider using weighted ropes only when you are in good physical condition. Weighted ropes like those shown in Fig-

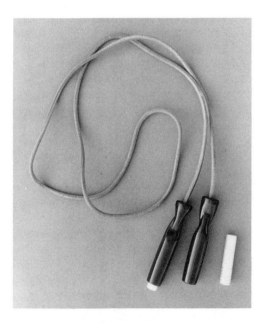

Figure 5.6   A leather jump rope with optional weights that can be inserted into the handles.

ure 5.7 make the arm and shoulder muscles work harder in order to improve their endurance even more than is possible with conventional ropes. These ropes usually use one of two basic design approaches: Add weight to the handles or add weight to the rope itself. Each has its own peculiarities. Ropes with weights in the handles work fine for basic jumping or techniques where you move your feet. Models with modest weights, like the ones pictured in Figure 5.6 and 5.7a, work fine also for techniques where the hands must move as with crosses and Low-Impact Techniques. Models with heavily weighted handles, however, make it more difficult to execute these techniques.

Ropes with the weight concentrated in the rope itself vary from one-third pound, like the rope in Figure 5.7a, which uses heavier segments, to 6 pounds, like the rope in Figure 5.7b. When the weight is concentrated in the rope itself, the work load increases quickly as the rope turns faster because the centrifugal force increases with speed. Ropes like that shown in Figure 5.7a can nicely firm the upper body while still being manageable at usual turning speeds. Athletes interested in developing upper body power would also benefit from speed jumping with moderately weighted ropes because they must develop strength and speed before they can acquire power.

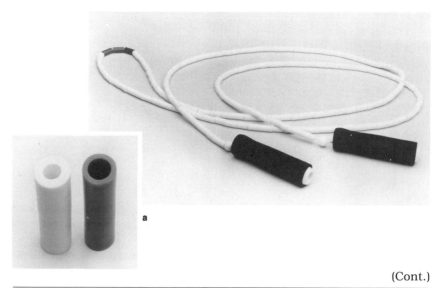

(Cont.)

Figure 5.7   (a) The Power Rope, made by Lifeline® , is heavier due to its thicker walled beads (see inset). (b) This Heavy Rope® model weighs 2 pounds. Some models weigh up to 6 pounds.

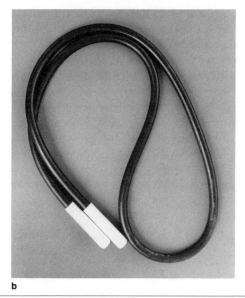

b

Figure 5.7   (Continued)

Heavier designs like the model illustrated in Figure 5.7b are made from solid rubber (e.g., Spaulding Sport Rope®) or sand-filled latex tubes (e.g., Heavy Rope®). The former design is preferable to the latter because it stretches much less and is more durable. However, either design will quickly tax your arms and your wind and they can only be used for short intervals even by strong individuals. Therefore, they should not be used for the Ropics program described later in the book.

Dressing for Exercise Success

The most expensive item you need to buy to begin Ropics is also the most important item in regard to safety—a good pair of aerobic dance or cross-training shoes. These types of shoes have cushioning and support under the ball of the foot, which is where you land when jumping properly. Be sure to buy a quality pair of shoes that fit your feet snugly. To be certain the shoes fit well, don't be afraid to give your shoes a test jump (without the rope) in the store. Poor shoe construction or improper fit will only increase the risk of costly injuries to feet, ankles, or knees.

Here are a few words about other types of footwear you might already have in the closet and be tempted to get by with for Ropics.

Running shoes have more cushion in the heels than the forefoot and don't provide the lateral support you need for many footwork techniques. Court shoes have good lateral support but generally have less forefoot cushioning for absorbing the shock of impact. Of course, you should forget about jumping rope in street shoes, most of which aren't even designed for walking. And avoid jumping rope while barefoot; a rope striking naked toes smarts!

Round out your outfit with athletic wear that doesn't restrict movement or prevent sweat from wicking away from the body. For support, women will want to wear an athletic bra and perhaps a leotard. Men should wear snug briefs or an athletic supporter. If you have long hair, you will want to keep it out of your eyes with a headband, hair clip, or rubber band. If you sweat profusely, consider wearing a headband to save your eyes from the sting of perspiration and wrist bands to help maintain your grip on the handles. See Figure 5.8 for a summary of a properly attired rope jumper.

Headband
Earphones

Lycra top over sport bra

Personal tape player or radio

Wristbands

Figure 5.8   Kathleen has all the accessories for a safe and fun, music-powered Ropics workout.

Moving to Music

Ropics and music are perfect partners. Not only does music induce the feet to start moving and the rope to start spinning, but the changing beats and rhythms also make it challenging and fun to vary rope techniques and speed. Pick whichever style of music makes you want to move. Pop, jazz, rap, swing, rock, and polka are just a few styles of music that fit Ropics well. Since the legs find it most comfortable to jump between 120 and 140 times a minute, it's especially helpful to choose music with a similar number of beats per minute. See Table 5.1 for a sample list of contemporary songs that work well for Ropics. Choose the selections with the slower beats per minute (bpm) for your warm-up and cool-down and the faster selections for the aerobic phase (see chapter 7 regarding workout design).

Since Ropics is essentially a stationary exercise program, any portable music system or boom box will work well in most circumstances. Some health clubs will also let you use the exercise studio

Table 5.1 **Some Recommended Music for Ropics**

Song Title	Artist	Label	bpm*
Warm-up and stretch			
"People Hold On"	Coldcut	Tommy Boy	124
"Get Up (Before the Night Is Over)"	Technotronic	SBK	124
"Dangerous"	Roxette	EMI	124
Aerobic phase			
"The Locomotion"	Kylie Minogue	Geffen	128
"Hangin' On the Boulevard"	Voyeur	CBS	128
"Scotland the Brave" (*Hooked on Classics II*)	The Royal Philharmonic Orchestra	RCA	132
"We Connect"	Stacey Q	Atlantic	132
"The Rumor"	Olivia Newton-John	MCA	132
"New Attitude"	Pattie LaBelle	MCA	136
Cool-down			
"Trouble"	Nia Peeples	Polygram	120
"Rocket 2 U" (extended mix)	The Jets	MCA	120
Final stretch			
"Silhouette"	Kenny G	Arista	Slow
"Spring Song"	Michael Jones	Narada	Slow

*bpm = beats per minute.

sound system if you've developed their trust. If, however, the sound from a boom box interferes with the activities of others, or if you do Ropics in a room with bad acoustics, like a racquetball court, you will want to consider a personal sound system like those made popular by the Sony Walkman® . These miniature units can provide excellent, stimulating sound for your workouts if you heed the tips listed in the box and illustrated in Figure 5.8.

How to Securely Wear a Personal Radio or Tape Player for Ropics Workouts

- The lighter and less bulky the unit, the less likely it is to bounce or interfere with arm movement. Radio-only models come especially small and might be a good choice if you have a local station that reliably plays motivating music. Cassette tape players are often worth their extra weight and expense since you can choose your own music. By placing the tape player on the *inside* of the waist band or wearing it on a nonelastic belt, you can prevent it from bouncing or flying off if you brush it with your arm. You can also buy belts with a pocket specially designed to hold personal players.

- If you decide on a tape player, be certain that it has an antiroll mechanism. This feature decreases speed variations in tape playback that can occur while jumping.

- Route the headphone wire under your shirt to keep it out of the way.

- The tiny earbud-type headphones, which fit almost entirely inside the ear, work particularly well for Ropics because they tend to stay in place despite vigorous movement. Wear a headband over the headphones if they don't stay in place while jumping.

Facilities and Floor Surfaces

Gymnasiums, exercise studios, racquetball or tennis courts, pool decks, rubberized running tracks, a vacant corner in the weight room, and nearly any large room are all possible places to do Ropics. As a minimum, you will need a 9-foot diameter area clear of obstructions and a 9-foot or higher ceiling. If there is any chance you might strike the chandelier or a family heirloom, go elsewhere.

The next important consideration is the floor. Not only can the floor affect how often you miss the rope, it can also have a significant affect on the injury rate, as the aerobic dance industry has learned. Therefore, certain floor companies have gone to great lengths to design the ideal floor with a suitable combination of shock absorption, energy return, and stability. These floors are generically referred to as *suspended* wood floors and can be found in dance and exercise studios. Suspended wood floors are also ideal for Ropics because they provide workouts biomechanically similar to mixed high- and low-impact aerobic dance. Admittedly, suspended floors aren't easy to find. Rubber tiled, polyurethane, and solid wood floors are also acceptable. Carpets with a low nap and a modest amount of padding are a third choice.

Thick napped or heavily padded carpets, which are found in many exercise studios and homes, are not well suited for rope jumping. Much like running in sand, your feet tend to sink into this surface and lose the spring needed for the next rebound. Not only is the work harder, but timing also suffers, which increases the chance for misses. If you have to jump on a carpet, place a plastic chair mat, like the ones used in offices, over the carpet. Be sure the mat has many cleats on the underside to prevent it from slipping. Now you have a stable surface that flexes a small amount but doesn't let your feet sink too much.

If you like to jump outdoors, asphalt has some give to it on warm days, but its rough surface wears out the middle of ropes rather quickly. Avoid concrete and hard-tiled floors because their unforgiving surfaces increase the risk of shin splints, sore calves, and other leg and foot injuries. If you have no other option, I strongly recommend that you get a mat to jump on to provide some cushion. A sports equipment catalog called *Sportime* makes a mat especially designed for this purpose and is listed in the appendix.

Wrap-Up

As with any activity, having the right equipment, apparel, and accessories can mean the difference between enjoyment and disappointment, or long-term safety and unexpected injury. The right jump rope(s), apparel, and music all help cultivate a smile with each workout. The right shoes and floor can help you keep that smile long after the workout.

CHAPTER 6

Getting and Staying Motivated

To be of lifelong benefit, you must practice Ropics, or any other exercise program for that matter, regularly and indefinitely. If you stop exercising or exercise infrequently (less than two or three times per week), your cardiovascular conditioning and muscular endurance will decrease up to 50% in 2 weeks. Within 2 months, certain areas of fitness will be back to where you started. Several studies have also shown that the health benefits of exercise also fade when you return to inactivity. For example, in 1986 Dr. Ralph Paffenbarger, along with a group of colleagues, reported the results of a now-famous study that showed that Harvard alumni who were athletes in college, but were no longer active, showed the same incidence of heart disease as their classmates who were never active. Conversely, alumni who kept active throughout their lives had a lower incidence of heart disease and lived longer than their sedentary counterparts whether they were a college athlete or not.

Strategies for Staying Motivated

Obviously, exercise requires a lifelong commitment—a commitment that can be trying to all but the most compulsive fitness fanatics. How then do mere mortals, like me and probably you, faithfully exercise at least twice and preferably three times a week ad infinitum? The following list of strategies can help you continue to look forward to each session with the rope whether it is day 1 or year 10.

• *For the umpteenth time: Take along your favorite dance music.* Enough said.

• *Join one of the jump rope organizations listed in the appendix.* Their membership fees are minimal, and those few dollars will give you access to shared experiences, ideas, camaraderie, and techniques unavailable at any other price.

• *Set specific, reasonable goals that you enjoy or take pride in attaining.* Most of our students enjoy setting their sights on mastering any of the endless number of techniques or their variations. For example, once you have the Two-Foot Jump under your belt, you could begin to work on the Swing Wrap or the Jogging Step or practice the Two-Foot Jump with the rope turning backward. Learning new techniques helps keep your mind preoccupied and does great things for your confidence. Also, if you use this approach, others will soon be impressed with your jump rope skills. A few other goals include jumping for speed (doing a technique as many times as possible in a period of time), jumping for endurance (doing a technique for as long as possible), working on accuracy (doing a technique until you miss), or putting together a flawless jump rope routine. If you decide to work on speed or endurance jumping, be certain that you are already in good physical condition.

• *Reward yourself for attaining your goals.* Have you finally mastered all Level 1 techniques? Have you successfully completed 100 Jogging Steps without a miss or, after many trials and tribulations, have you completed your Front Cross? Pat yourself on the back with a new compact disc, jump rope, leotard, visit to your favorite restaurant, or whatever other reward will motivate you.

• *Keep a calendar of the days you do or plan to do Ropics and record your specific accomplishments or target dates.* This strategy will give you a yardstick for measuring how far you've come and where you're going, whether it's losing pounds, gaining endurance, or mastering skills.

• *Avoid working out every day.* Daily exercise, especially if intense, can lead to chronic fatigue and decreased enthusiasm over time. Your body simply needs occasional rest to restore energy supplies and make minor mends.

• *Vary your routine.* If stationary exercise machines have a downfall, it's that, short of moving them to another room, you cannot greatly vary your routine. Besides doing different techniques, you can add spice to Ropics in many other ways:

  • *Vary the location.* For example, on a nice day, take the rope outside to the boardwalk, tennis court, or wood deck.
  • *Exchange fellowship, ideas, techniques, and enthusiasm with other jump rope enthusiasts.*
  • *Try different types of music.*

- *Alternate Ropics with other exercise programs.* In the summer, you might add bicycling or jogging. In the winter, you might add racquetball. You can also easily mix in aerobic dance to alternate with your Ropics sessions.

Wrap-Up

You undoubtedly have many other ideas about what motivates you, and I encourage you to put them to work. The key points to sticking with exercise are to make it an experience that you look forward to, and to track your progress. Chapter 7 gives you more specific points on how to make each Ropics workout as enjoyable and beneficial as possible.

CHAPTER 7

Putting Ropics to Work for You

The Ropics program is intended to minimize injuries and discouraging aches, pains, and exhaustion while maximizing benefits, efficiency, and enjoyment. Ropics accomplishes this by guiding you through the following phases of a workout:

- Warm-up
- Stretching
- Skill development
- Workout or aerobic
- Cool-down

Remember, however, that even the best designed program is only a guide. It is impossible to design a program perfect for everyone because everyone is different. Your own body must be your ultimate boss—which, as you will see, the Ropics program encourages. As before, get clearance from a physician before starting Ropics if you have health problems or heart disease risk factors or you are over 35 years old (see page 35).

General Rules

How can your body, which you may not have subjected to serious exercise since childhood, guide you through a new experience like Ropics? A large part of the answer is simply to listen to your body. First, Ropics should not be an exercise that causes discomfort. The recent axiom of No pain, no gain applies primarily to competitive athletes who are pushing for that extra bit of physical performance, not to a person whose goal is simply to be healthy and physically fit. If something hurts, *stop* and reexamine what you are doing. Ropics shouldn't make you feel breathless during the workout, nor sore and aching the next day. If either condition occurs, your enthusiasm is probably pushing you harder than what the program recommends. Again, stop immediately, and see your doctor if you experience any of these warning signs:

- Chest, neck, jaw, shoulder, or arm discomfort
- Nausea or indigestion
- Dizziness
- Palpitations (sensation of a racing or irregular heart beat)
- Shortness of breath not immediately relieved with rest
- Pain not relieved with rest or still present after 1 day

Another important tool for guiding yourself through exercise is knowledge. If you understand how and why a program is put together, then you will be better prepared to fine-tune it for yourself. The following pages give the information you need to make Ropics work for you.

A Ropics Workout

Each Ropics workout consists of five sections that flow into one another: warm-up, stretching, skill development, aerobic phase, and cool-down. Let me review the hows and whys of each important section.

Priming the Systems—The Warm-Up

Sudden, increased demands in movement and work intensity pose greater stress to the body, and hence greater risk of injury, than when those demands are gradually increased. Therefore, 5 to 10 minutes of light exercise, or a warm-up, should precede all other parts of a workout. Exercises appropriate for the warm-up include calisthenics, easy jogging or bicycling, Low-Impact Techniques, and even basic rope jumping when you've become experienced. Throughout this phase, gradually increase the exercise intensity, but never to the point of feeling more than moderate exertion (see page 74). The warm-up derives its name from the fact that this phase slightly elevates the body's temperature. Research indicates that warmed muscles are more elastic and therefore less prone to injury. The warm-up serves other purposes as well. The heart rate, breathing rate, and blood circulation to the muscles increase to ready the body's energy systems for the more active exercise to follow.

The warm-up serves one other purpose that is especially important for skilled activities like rope jumping—it primes the nervous system for the timing, rhythm, and coordination subtleties unique to the activity. It's no coincidence that all types of athletes, from basketball players to figure skaters, rehearse their sport before jumping into the game or competition. Thus, after your first Ropics workout, you should include Low-Impact Techniques and a little basic jumping in your warm-up.

Stretching It Out

An important element of fitness is flexibility, which is best attained through proper stretching. As discussed in chapter 3, the flexibility gained through proper stretching decreases the risk of muscle strains and certain other types of injury. If you are an athlete in an activity that requires flexibility like gymnastics, dance, karate, swimming, and even advanced rope jumping, stretching can also better your athletic performance.

Figures 7.1 through 7.10 illustrate different stretching exercises that will increase the flexibility of most major muscle groups important for Ropics. The stretches shown should all be held for 15 to 30 seconds at a position where you feel mild tension in the muscle, but no burning pain. You should repeat each stretch at least twice. Concentrate on relaxing the stretched muscle, and be sure to breathe normally rather than holding your breath. Always be aware of proper posture when stretching, and avoid forcing any stretch position just to look like the models. To avoid injury, be your own judge as to what your final position will be.

If you would like to learn more about stretching, read a book devoted to it like Judy Alter's *Stretch & Strengthen* (see Bibliography) or either of Michael Alter's stretching books: *Science of Stretching* or *Sport Stretch.*

TORSO STRETCH

Figure 7.1

Stand with feet shoulder-width apart and with knees slightly bent. Keep the lower back vertical to lessen back strain. Bend torso to the left, place left hand on top of left thigh to support your weight. Reach right hand diagonally up and across to the left. Be sure to relax shoulders as you reach to the side for 15 to 30 seconds. Repeat on the other side.

BACK OF SHOULDER (POSTERIOR DELTOID) STRETCH

Figure 7.2

Stand with feet shoulder-width apart and with knees slightly bent. Gently pull right elbow horizontally across the chest toward left shoulder and hold. Repeat on the other side.

BACK OF UPPER ARM (TRICEPS) STRETCH

Figure 7.3

Stand with feet shoulder-width apart and with knees slightly bent. Bring both arms overhead and hold right elbow with left hand. Slowly, gently pull right elbow behind the head. Reverse to stretch left arm.

FRONT OF SHOULDER AND CHEST
(ANTERIOR DELTOID AND PECTORALIS) STRETCH

Figure 7.4

Stand with feet shoulder-width apart and with knees slightly bent. Interlace fingers behind the back, keeping elbows bent at all times. Gently lift both arms up behind you and hold for 15 to 30 seconds.

UPPER CALF (GASTROCNEMIUS) STRETCH

Figure 7.5

Stand with the left foot forward, toes pointing directly forward. Extend the right leg straight back. Attempt to press the right heel toward the floor. Flex or bend the left knee as shown. Reverse to stretch left calf. (Note: Whenever you bend your knees, keep them directly over the toes.)

LOWER CALF (SOLEUS) STRETCH AND HEEL CORD (ACHILLES' TENDON) STRETCH

Figure 7.6

Start in the same position as above. Gently lift back right heel off the floor allowing right knee to bend. Shift your weight slightly onto back leg and hold. Slowly change sides after 15 to 30 seconds.

SHIN (ANTERIOR TIBIALIS) STRETCH

Figure 7.7

From a standing position gently point right foot forward keeping right knee in line with toes. Hold this position with right heel off the floor. Slowly change sides.

FRONT OF HIP (HIP FLEXOR) STRETCH

Figure 7.8

Stand with left knee bent and directly above toes of left foot. Lean torso forward and slowly extend right leg back, keeping knee in line with toes. Begin with hands on left thigh and slowly shift weight back onto the ball of right foot. (Think of lowering your pelvis down to the floor.) You may want to place your hands on either side of the forward leg for a deeper stretch. Slowly change sides after 15 to 30 seconds.

FRONT OF THIGH (QUADRICEPS) STRETCH

Figure 7.9

Sit on the floor with pelvis facing front. Bring right knee in front of you with the outside of the leg resting on the floor. Bend right knee 90 degrees. Bring left leg directly to your side off left hip. Rest the inside of left leg on the floor. Bend left knee 90 degrees. Lean upper body back and to the right, resting on right forearm. Keep your stomach muscles tight; do not arch your back. Hold for 15 to 30 seconds then change sides. (If you don't feel a stretch in this position, press left hip toward the floor.)

BACK OF THIGH (HAMSTRING) STRETCH

Figure 7.10

Lie on your back with knees bent and with soles of feet on the floor. Bring left knee to the chest. Gently extend left knee and hold where you feel slight tension. Do not let the hip or back of head come up off the floor. Slowly change legs after 15 to 30 seconds.

Skill Development

After you've warmed up and stretched is a good time to learn new jump rope techniques. The body is now prepared for the work involved in learning a new skill. You can also choose to learn new techniques during the aerobic phase as long as you're not so tired that the learning process is hindered. Refer to the technique instruction sections in Part III, and decide where you need to start. Of course, unless you are already quite experienced with the jump rope, start at the beginning—learning how to turn the rope and jump properly.

In reality, skill development actually takes place throughout most phases of a workout. While most techniques are learned relatively quickly, they usually take repeated practice to truly *master*. Therefore, you will be gradually refining your jump rope skills whenever you incorporate a technique into any section of the workout.

The Aerobic Phase

Once you have a few jump rope techniques under your belt, you're ready for the meat of the workout—the aerobic phase. During the aerobic phase, you will put the jump rope to work to get your body in shape. Table 7.1 should be your guide to this part of the workout for the next few months. To use the table, first find the section that was developed for your age group (column 1). Then, locate the line that indicates the number of weeks you have been doing Ropics (column 2). Reading across this line, find the suggested duration, frequency, intensity, and RJT-to-LIT ratio of the aerobic phase for that week. Let me explain what each column means.

Duration

Column 3 indicates how long the aerobic phase should be in a given week (this is in addition to the warm-up, skill development, and cool-down phases). The workouts are of short duration in the beginning of the program to allow your body to adapt gradually to the new demands of exercise. Over time, the workouts eventually reach 20 to 30 minutes. That's all the time you ever need to exercise to achieve optimum health and physical fitness. Longer workouts are only necessary for competitive athletes seeking a higher level of performance. A common misconception is that you need to exercise for 1/2 hour on the first day—a strategy that often leads to aches and soreness.

Table 7.1 **The Ropics Program Aerobic Phase***

Age (years)	Week of program	Duration (minutes)	Frequency (×/week)	Exercise intensity	
				RPE scale	Suggested RJT:LIT
12-29	1-2	10	4-5	3-5	1:1
	3-4	12	4-5	3-5	2:1
	5-8	15	3-5	4-5	2:1
	9-12	20	3-5	4-5	3:1
	13-	20-30	3-5	4-5	**
30-39	1-2	10	4-5	3-5	1:1
	3-4	12	4-5	3-5	2:1
	5-8	15	3-5	4-5	2:1
	9-12	20	3-5	4-5	3:1
	13-	20-30	3-5	4-5	**
40-49	1-2	10	4-5	3-4	1:1
	3-4	12	4-5	3-5	2:1
	5-6	15	3-5	4-5	2:1
	7-8	15	3-5	4-5	3:1
	8-16	20	3-5	4-5	3:1
	17-	20-30	3-5	4-5	**
50-59	1-3	7	4-5	3-4	1:1
	4-6	10	4-5	3-4	1:1
	7-8	12	4-5	3-4	2:1
	9-12	15	3-5	3-4	2:1
	13-16	20	3-5	3-5	3:1
	17-	20-25	3-5	3-5	**
60 until	1-4	5	4-5	3-4	1:1
weight-bearing	5-8	7	4-5	3-4	1:1
exercise no	9-10	10	4-5	3-4	2:1
longer	11-14	12	3-5	3-4	2:1
recommended	15-18	15	3-5	3-5	3:1
by doctor	19-	15-20	3-5	3-5	**

*See your physician before beginning any exercise program.

**By this point in the program, you should know how your body responds to Ropics and be able to mix LITs and RJTs at your own discretion.

Frequency

Column 4 gives the suggested number of Ropics workouts per week. Since the aerobic phase is short the first few weeks, we recommend at least four workouts per week to ensure progress in your fitness and skills. After the first 1 or 2 months, you need to work out only three times over the course of a week to maintain optimal fitness. If you exercise less than three times a week, your fitness might not improve, and if you are already fit, you face the real possibility of slowly losing fitness.

Conversely, exercising too often, especially at high intensities or for long durations, is also counterproductive. If you don't give your body a rest at least a couple of times a week, you increase the chances of overuse injuries like shin splints and tendinitis. You also run the risk of physical and mental stagnation or *burnout*—a decline in performance or enthusiasm due to overtraining.

Exercise Intensity

How hard your body is working at any particular time is referred to as *exercise intensity*. Columns 5 and 6 are concerned with guiding the exercise intensity of your Ropics sessions. I am going to spend a little time discussing these columns because they are important in helping you avoid soreness and early fatigue and are not as intuitive as duration and frequency.

The RPE Scale.   Most exercise programs guide the intensity of your workouts by having you check your heart rate, which is reflected by your pulse. The harder you exercise, the faster your heart rate and your pulse. Several studies have shown, however, that the heart rate does not accurately measure the exercise intensity for rope jumping (nor for aerobic dance, a similar activity). Fortunately, another scientifically proven method exists for measuring intensity. It has many advantages over checking the heart rate including its simplicity.

Your own senses give you an accurate indication of exercise intensity. Somehow the brain weighs the various signals from your heart, lungs, muscles, and other systems to give you an overall picture of just how hard you are exercising. Dr. Gunnar Borg of Sweden formulated a simple scale called the Rated Perceived Exertion (RPE) scale (Table 7.2) to help you put a number on how hard you feel like you are exerting yourself. For example, during a casual walk, chances are that you would feel as though your level of exertion is *very slight* or a 1 on a scale of 0 to 10. A rating of 9 or 10 would be appropriate if you were running from an angry bear.

For Ropics, you want to adjust the vigorousness of your workouts so that your sense of exertion is between 3 (moderate) and 5 (strong). If you don't feel as though you are exerting yourself after a few minutes of exercise, you need to work a little harder to raise the intensity to at least a 3. Conversely, if you can't talk comfortably while exercising, you are definitely exerting yourself beyond

Table 7.2 **Rated Perceived Exertion (RPE) Scale**

0	Nothing at all
0.5	Extremely slight
1	Very slight
2	Slight
3	Moderate
4	Somewhat strong
5	Strong
6	
7	Very strong
8	
9	Extremely strong
10	Maximal

Note. From "Psychophysical Bases of Perceived Exertion" by G.V. Borg, 1982, *Medicine and Science in Sports and Exercise*, **14**(5), p. 378. Copyright 1982 by *Medicine and Science in Sports and Exercise.* Reprinted by permission.

5 and should back off on the intensity. By the way, if you don't feel winded but your calves or some other parts of your body are saying, "Hey, it's a 9 down here!" decrease the intensity. By keeping the intensity in the 3 to 5 range, your fitness will improve without undue exhaustion or risk of injury.

Besides the simplicity, the RPE scale has several other advantages over checking your pulse. First, you don't have to stop the rope, find your pulse in your wrist or neck, count for 10 to 15 seconds, start the rope again, and then repeat the process later. With the RPE scale, all you need to do is glance at the table from time to time and make the necessary adjustments. (In the beginning, you can copy the scale with a magic marker onto a piece of paper and tape it to a wall where you exercise. After a while, you can just picture the scale in your mind.) Second, as already mentioned, the RPE scale takes into account the weakest link in your body. If you are already in good condition, but not used to constant jumping, your calves might need a break before the rest of your body does.

The principal disadvantage of the RPE scale is that you must learn to monitor and trust the signals your body is sending to you about the work load. Many beginners are so excited about their new venture that they ignore their senses and push themselves to the limit on the first day. Then they cry "Woe is me!" on the following 4 days. The muscles ache, the joints feel stiff, and the body in general feels 20 years older—giving the beginner the wrong impression that his or her body is not made for exercise. Remember, it's better to be conservative in regard to exercise intensity until you know exactly how your body responds to the various demands.

Suggested RJT:LIT.   All this talk about decreasing the exercise intensity would be for naught if Ropics were a traditional jump rope program. As discussed in chapter 2, *prolonged* rope jumping at even a slow rate is too taxing for the average beginner. Fortunately, Ropics provides an out. Ropics divides jump rope techniques into two major divisions: Techniques that require jumping are called *Rope Jumping Techniques* (RJTs), and techniques that do not require any jumping are called *Low-Impact Techniques* (LITs).

LITs generally require much less energy than RJTs and give the legs a break from jumping while still allowing you to keep moving with the rope. By alternating bouts of LITs with short bouts of RJTs, you can tailor a Ropics workout to fit your present level of fitness. For example, in week 1, column 6 recommends that you do a 1:1 ratio of RJTs to LITs. You might alternate 20 Two-Foot Jumps (RJT) with 20 Figure-Eights (LIT). If you don't like to count, you could do 10 to 30 seconds of Jogging Steps (RJT) and then 10 to 30 seconds of Windmills (LIT). And, if you are not a clock watcher either, you could do RJTs to the verses in a song and do LITs to the chorus. As your fitness and skills with the rope improve, you increase the time spent jumping, which increases the ratio of RJTs to LITs. Again, the ratios given in Table 7.1 are only suggestions. Using the RPE scale and listening to your body's own signals can help you adjust the intervals even better than adhering to the suggested RJT:LIT ratio.

Although you might currently have doubts, most people can eventually do basic rope jumping for 15 minutes without a second thought. LITs are rarely abandoned completely, however, since they are fun, add variety, and provide a welcome respite after doing some of the more advanced and demanding RJTs like Double Unders.

Cooling Down

Just as you should warm up before a vigorous workout, so you should cool down afterward. A cool-down should consist of about 5 minutes of lower intensity exercise similar to the warm-up: calisthenics, easy jogging, easy jumping, and/or LITs. The purpose of the cool-down is to avoid a sudden change in exercise intensity that puts an extra stress on your heart. In fact, physicians have their patients lie down immediately after a treadmill stress test to see if there are any danger flags during what the heart considers to be the most stressful part of the test.

There is also at least one other benefit to a cool-down. Lactic acid, a waste product of exercise found in the blood and muscles, is metabolized more quickly during low-intensity exercise than during rest.

It's a nice touch to conclude a workout with some easy stretching as illustrated before. The muscles are even warmer now than after the warm-up, so this is a great time to improve your flexibility further. Slow, measured, stretching exercises also help you to relax after an invigorating Ropics workout.

Wrap-Up

Putting it all together, there are five parts to a Ropics workout: 1) warm-up, 2) stretching, 3) skill development, 4) aerobic phase, and 5) cool-down. Each plays an important role in maximizing the benefits and/or decreasing the risk of injury. Figure 7.11 shows how this approach also gradually increases and decreases the exercise intensity to avoid stressing the body with sudden change. The figure also shows how RJTs and LITs raise and lower exercise intensity, respectively, during the aerobic phase. An entire workout should take between 35 and 45 minutes once you reach the maintenance level. In the beginning, your workouts will be of shorter duration. Ropics or other types of aerobic exercise should be done at

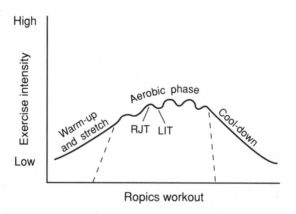

Figure 7.11   Including a proper warm-up and cool-down prevents subjecting your body to a sudden change in exercise intensity. The dashed lines represent the sudden changes in exercise intensity without a warm-up and cool-down.

least three times a week. Realize that this is asking you to devote only 1.05% of your week to benefit the other 98.95%. Not a bad deal!

Finally, remember to listen to your body. If you are exercising to enhance your health and physical fitness and not to win an Olympic gold medal, then there is no need for profuse sweating, aching muscles, and lost breath. Have the RPE scale handy and keep your level of exertion between 3 and 5 by alternating periods of RJTs with LITs.

Now that you know how to put a safe, effective jump rope workout together and have your equipment and music all set, it's time to become acquainted with the versatile (and exciting) jump rope.

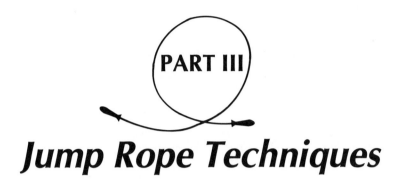

Jump Rope Techniques

Over the centuries, people around the world have created literally thousands of ways to jump rope. This book teaches only those variations where one person uses a short jump rope. (Other variations involving long ropes or more than one person such as Double Dutch and the Chinese Wheel are not included here since they are of less interest to adults.) The techniques illustrated in the following chapters represent a cross-section of skills that will give you a broad, solid foundation for even more growth. (Look back at Table 2.1 (page 15) to remind yourself of the Ropics technique divisions.)

Ropics divides techniques in two ways. First, they are divided by how they are executed. If the technique does not require you to jump over the rope, it is placed in the Low-Impact Technique (LIT) division. If jumping is required, then the technique is placed in the Rope Jumping Technique (RJT) division. Second, to help you with learning and motivation, Ropics divides techniques according to level of difficulty. The most basic techniques are assigned to Level 1. Levels 2 through 5 include progressively more challenging techniques. This book includes examples of techniques from the first three levels because these are the most practical for an exercise program. To give you an even better idea of how challenging a technique is, we also assign a difficulty factor (DF) to it. The larger the DF, the more challenging the technique. In assigning a DF, we weighed how much the technique required from the following areas:

- Coordination/agility
- Strength
- Timing and rhythmic skill
- Flexibility

Of course, the DF is meant only as a general guide. Doing a technique on your weaker side or in a backward direction can increase

the technique's difficulty. Also, depending on individual experience and talent, a technique that is challenging for one person
might come easily for another.

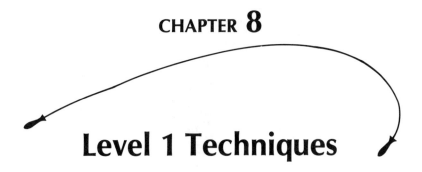

CHAPTER 8

Level 1 Techniques

Although Level 1 techniques are technically the easiest to do, in many ways they are the most challenging to learn. Not only will you be developing a number of important fundamental skills, but this stage is also critical for developing your confidence. To help you gain that confidence, here's a step-by-step approach for learning how to do the most basic Rope Jumping Technique. You'll also learn a basic Low-Impact Technique along the way.

Learning the Basic Two-Foot Jump (DF = 1.2)

Before learning the new skills, be sure to warm up with your favorite form of light exercise and stretch as discussed earlier.

Step 1: Turning the Rope

Hold the rope with both handles in your dominant hand as pictured in Figure 8.1. Now, with your forearms angled out about 45 degrees, turn the rope at your side in a forward direction. Remember that the rope approaches the toes before the heels when it is turning *forward*. Use wrist and forearm action to turn the rope. If your arm is making big circles, you are using your shoulder, which looks and feels awkward and increases the work load.

When you feel comfortable turning the rope in one hand, practice with the other hand. By the way, besides practicing how to turn the rope, you are also learning an LIT called Windmills (DF = 1.0).

Figure 8.1

Step 2: Proper Jumping Form

Even though the second step might seem absurdly simple, proper jumping skills require some practice for most people. Begin by jumping just once at a time, without a rope, while keeping the following form points in mind:

• The feet should stay together and directly underneath your body (i.e., *don't kick back*).

• Jump only 1 inch or less off the ground (the rope is skinny) and land lightly on the balls of your feet. If you hear yourself land, you are jumping too high or landing with too much force.

• Look straight ahead and maintain a good, erect posture.

Repeat several times until you have the correct form as shown in Figure 8.2 and feel as though you are jumping as lightly as possible.

Now, work on rhythmic jumping. This is a good time to put on one of those songs listed in Table 5.1 for motivation. The legs find it most comfortable to jump between 120 and 140 times per minute so choose a song with similar beats per minute (bpm). Keeping the jumping form described previously, jump lightly up and down. Keep the RPE scale handy and listen to your legs to be certain you don't overpractice. If you begin to feel that you are exerting yourself beyond 5, pick up a rope and practice Step 1 (Windmills) until you have recovered. Your feet should slightly leave the ground with

Figure 8.2

every jump. You've got Step 2 down when you can jump lightly and comfortably while maintaining good form.

Step 3: Jumping in Time to the Rope

Now it's time to combine Steps 1 and 2. Turn the rope at your side in a forward direction with the dominant hand as in Figure 8.3. As the rope approaches the ground, jump softly as you did in Step 2. When you have mastered jumping in time to the rope while using your dominant hand, practice jumping and turning the rope in your other hand.

As before, go back to Windmills if you begin to feel as though you are going beyond 5 on the RPE scale. This time, however, march in place while doing Windmills.

Figure 8.3

Step 4: Actually Jumping Over the Rope

Now for the real thing! Grab a handle with each hand and place the rope at your heels. Swing the rope over your head and jump as it approaches your toes while keeping the good form you've been practicing all along and reemphasized in Figure 8.4. The rope should make one turn for each jump.

If you jumped rope as a child, you might have a tendency to *jump bounce* or make a small rebound jump in between each turn of the rope. Fight this habit by turning the rope a little faster. There is nothing technically wrong with jump bouncing, but this habit does make it more difficult to develop other skills.

When you first begin jumping over the rope, you might also still have a tendency to jump high, kick the feet back or use the shoulders despite your earlier practice. If you stick with it and make a conscious effort to develop good form, however, you will look like a pro within a few sessions, perhaps sooner.

As always, don't become so enthusiastic that you overdo it and wake up discouraged with aches the next morning. Alternate brief bouts of jumping with Windmills while marching in place. An example of a Level 1 workout follows. This particular workout is for those who have been practicing Ropics for a couple of weeks.

a   b

Figure 8.4

SAMPLE LEVEL 1 ROPICS WORKOUT

Warm-Up

Before you start your workout, be sure you have the appropriate music ready for each phase (refer to Table 5.1). Gradually increase exercise intensity over 4 to 5 minutes by alternating intervals of Figure-Eights and Windmills with brief intervals of Two-Foot Jumps.

Stretching

Spend 5 to 10 minutes stretching, using the techniques illustrated on pages 66-70.

Skill Development

Practice the Twist and Leg Over Pass for several minutes.

Aerobic Phase

Alternate intervals of the Two-Foot Jump, Twist, and Skier (Level 1 RJTs) with intervals of Windmills, Figure-Eights, Leg Over Passes, and Swing Wraps (Level 1 LITs). See Table 7.1 for the recommended duration, intensity, and RJT:LIT ratio during the aerobic phase. By now, your RJT intervals might be longer than your LIT intervals. Be sure to listen to your body and use the RPE scale (Table 7.2) to determine how long or intense to make your RJT intervals.

Cool-Down

Gradually decrease the exercise intensity over 5 minutes by increasing the time spent doing LITs compared to RJTs, or switch to light jogging then brisk walking. End the session with some slow stretches to relaxing music.

Congratulations! You've just bettered your fitness in nearly every way possible.

General Tips for Learning Other Techniques

The hardest part is over, especially psychologically, when you've learned the Two-Foot Jump. Over 35 other techniques and variations follow, each with its own challenges and rewards. The following paragraphs will help you master nearly every one of them.

• The most important tip is: *Do not become discouraged if you miss* repeatedly while trying to learn a technique. As Figure 8.5 shows, even the best jump rope enthusiast gets tangled in the rope at times. If you begin to get frustrated, try it again on another day.

Figure 8.5   Even the best enthusiast gets tangled in the rope. The good rope jumpers don't give up!

• For RJTs, *learn the technique step by step.* For example, with the Twist (see page 91), practice the movement without the rope first. Next turn the rope at your side while doing the movement, and finally, jump over the rope. Variations on this theme will work for most RJTs; the text will help guide you. Because LITs are usually harder to break into steps, you must instead steadily build upon earlier LIT skills.

• Until you become experienced, *turn the rope in a forward direction* (so the rope approaches the toes before the heels) and at a moderate speed. Turning the rope backward or with speed is more difficult for most people.

• *Learn the techniques in the approximate order of their difficulty factor*, that is, learn the easier skills first. Front Crosses are undoubtedly already tempting you, but you should gain experience with a number of techniques that have a lower DF first.

• *Work on mastering only one or two techniques in the same time period.* Attempting to learn too many skills at once can become frustrating.

- *With each RJT you learn, also learn or practice an LIT.* This gives you something less demanding to work on when you become fatigued from jumping.

- Despite our best efforts, it is sometimes difficult to capture fully a technique with photography. If you have trouble visualizing how a technique is done, *consider ordering the Ropics video series*, which teaches the same techniques contained in this book (see the appendix). The Ropics video series also includes follow-along classes from warm-up to cool-down and a few routines so you can see how the techniques can all flow together. You may be surprised to see how even simple techniques like Windmills and Arm Wraps can look fascinating in the hands of an experienced enthusiast.

Representative Level 1 Low-Impact Techniques

WINDMILLS (DF = 1.0)

a   b   c

Figure 8.6

You've already practiced at least one Windmill variation while learning the Two-Foot Jump. The key point again is to turn the rope in a circle with the wrists and forearms, not the shoulders.

Many Windmill variations exist since the rope can be turned on any side (right, left, front, back, overhead), in two rotational directions (forward and backward), and with either or both hands. Figure 8.6a shows a Side Windmill to the left; Figure 8.6b shows a two-handed Front Windmill; and Figure 8.6c shows a one-handed Overhead Windmill (or Helicopter). Don't let the simplicity of Windmills fool you. Add a little speed and style, and they can look snappy. Also, Windmills are useful in teaching you how to manipulate and get a feel for the rope anywhere around the body.

Eddie Race is our senior rope jumping dynamo and is a walking (or jumping) advertisement for the vitality and vigor you can enjoy in your senior years if you keep active. Eddie constantly draws other people to rope jumping with his enthusiasm and by doing demonstrations at local events. He's also notorious for beating people 50 years his junior in his 10-second speed drills.

FIGURE-EIGHTS (DF = 1.3)

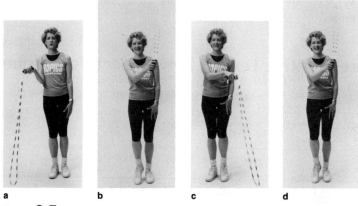

a   b   c   d

Figure 8.7

Turn the rope at one side and alternately change sides so that the rope travels in an 8 pattern. You could view Figure-Eights as Windmills that alternate from side to side. Again, practice with the rope turning in a forward direction first.

You can also do Figure-Eights with both hands. Two-handed Figure-Eights are often used for transitions between techniques and as a prelude to jumping since parting the hands will allow you to begin jumping with a live rope that is already up to speed.

Carol Roen has three children and began doing Ropics 1-1/2 years ago to add more variety and challenges to her aerobic workouts. She notes that Ropics has strengthened and firmed her legs while also improving her coordination for other activities. She also likes the fun and social aspects of belonging to the National Ropics Precision Team.

SWING WRAP (DF = 1.4)

a   b   c   d

Figure 8.8

Begin with a one-handed Overhead Windmill using the dominant hand (8.8a). As the rope comes forward, bring the hand down to waist level (8.8b) so the rope lightly wraps around the waist (8.8c, d). Pull the rope back to reverse the rotation for another Overhead Windmill or go into an entirely different technique. Wraps are one of several methods for reversing rope rotation.

FOOT CATCH (DF = 1.4)

a   b   c   d

Figure 8.9

As Figures 8.9a and 8.9b show, when the rope is turning forward, the middle of the rope is caught by lifting the toes up as the rope approaches the foot. The heel is lifted, as in Figures 8.9c and 8.9d, if the rope is turning backward. This technique is a nice way to end a routine or to stop the rope for reversing direction. A clever way out of a Foot Catch, called the Foot Flick, is taught with the Level 2 techniques.

DEMONSTRATOR PROFILE:

Ken Solis (author). You've already heard enough about me in other sections of the book. Hope you're having fun!

LEG OVER PASS (DF = 1.7)

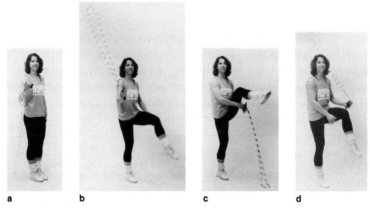

a   b   c   d

Figure 8.10

Here's an eye-catching way to switch rope ends from hand to hand. In preparation for the Leg Over Pass, be certain that you can exchange the rope ends to the other hand while doing one-handed Figure-Eights. When ready, continue the Figure-Eights, but pass the rope under the opposite lifted leg to the other hand. Of course, you may also pass the rope in the other direction.

DEMONSTRATOR PROFILE:

Kathleen Hargarten, MD, is a codeveloper of Ropics, coordinator of the National Ropics Precision Team, mother of three, and an assistant professor of trauma and emergency medicine. (Whew!) Besides keeping her fit, Ropics classes give her a relief from the stresses of working in a hectic trauma department.

Representative Level 1 Rope Jumping Techniques

SKIER (DF = 1.3)

a   b   c   d

Figure 8.11

As with downhill skiing, jump about 1/2 foot from side to side while keeping your feet together. Note that the rope makes it around without catching the toes because the feet are underneath the body when the rope passes under (8.11a,d). This is the case for most RJTs.

DEMONSTRATOR PROFILE:

Bob Stenzel, who is now 18 years old, has performed with The Wizards jump rope team from coast to coast since third grade. Also a veteran varsity basketball, baseball, and football player, he never intends to stop rope jumping and hopes that freestyle rope jumping will eventually become a competitive sport for adults.

TWIST (DF = 1.4)

a   b   c   d

Figure 8.12

As the name implies, you must keep your feet together while you twist at the waist from side to side. Beginners may want to twist only half way with each jump instead of doing a full twist as Bob is doing. (Get out the Chubby Checker record!)

JOGGING STEP (DF = 1.8)

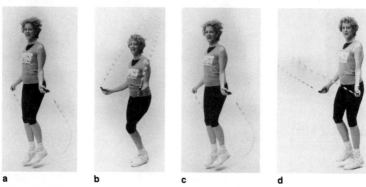

a   b   c   d

Figure 8.13

Like a light jog, lightly push off alternating feet with each turn of the rope. You'll note that Carol has her weight on the right foot in 8.13b and has shifted her weight to her left foot with the next jump as in 8.13d. It takes a little more practice to master than the Two-Foot Jump as the DF indicates. It is well worth the trouble, however, because it is the most efficient way to jump rope and is, therefore, the RJT used most frequently by experienced rope jumpers.

CHAPTER 9

Level 2 Techniques

With Level 1 techniques, the primary focus was on developing fundamental skills and cultivating confidence in your ability to master the jump rope. With Level 2, the focus is on further refining your skills and coaxing your confidence to grow even more.

At this point in your skill development, you can also begin experimenting with the rope rather than restricting yourself solely to what is written in this book. For example, although you can't tell from still photography, all the techniques are demonstrated with the rope turning forward. Most people find doing the techniques with the rope turning backward a little more challenging. Also, techniques that are illustrated as being done from one side, like the Matador Open, can always be done to the other side. Thus, four variations of a Matador Open exist: forward and to the right, forward and to the left, backward and to the right, and backward and to the left. As you can see, even the simplest techniques can keep you occupied for some time.

Another fruitful endeavor is to combine techniques. For example, you can combine a Front Cross (DF = 2.9) with a Cross Step (DF = 2.6). The combination is more difficult than either alone, but the point is to use your imagination to create new challenges. An example of a Level 2 workout that could be used after about a month of practice follows.

SAMPLE LEVEL 2 ROPICS WORKOUT

Warm-Up

Before you begin your workout, be sure to have the appropriate music ready for each phase (refer to Table 5.1). Gradually increase workout intensity over 5 to 10 minutes by alternating intervals of Level 1 LITs with brief intervals of Level 1 RJTs.

Stretching

Spend 5 to 10 minutes stretching using the techniques illustrated on pages 66-70.

Skill Development

Practice the Front Straddle and Matador Whirl for several minutes.

Aerobic Phase

Alternate intervals of Level 1 and 2 RJTs that you've mastered (e.g., Two-Foot Jump, Jogging Step, Side Straddles, and Scissors) with intervals of Level 1 and 2 LITs you're proficient at (e.g., Windmills, Figure-Eights, Forearm Wrap, and Samurai Whirl). You may choose to do only one technique during an entire interval or mix techniques in the same division. See Table 7.1 for the recommended duration, intensity, and RJT:LIT ratio during the aerobic phase. Be sure to listen to your body and use the RPE scale (Table 7.2) to guide the intensity and duration of your intervals. An interval that includes more demanding techniques like Front Straddles will need to be shorter than one that includes only less demanding techniques like the Jogging Step.

Cool-Down

Gradually decrease the exercise intensity over 5 minutes by increasing the time spent doing LITs compared to RJTs or switch to light jogging then brisk walking. End the session with some slow stretches to relaxing music.

Keep it up! By now people look up to you as an experienced jump rope enthusiast and are beginning to wonder if you take boxing lessons also.

Representative Level 2 Low-Impact Techniques

FOREARM WRAP (DF = 2.0)

a   b   c   d

Figure 9.1

Turn the rope at the right side with both hands (9.1a). Extend the right arm, and the rope will wrap around it (9.1b,c). To help with control, place the left hand near the right mid-forearm. To unwrap, reverse the arm rotation when the wrap is complete. As with all Wrap techniques, the rope turns in the opposite direction after completion.

A more interesting option for unwrapping the rope is to bring the right arm across the chest to the left side (91.d) at any point during the wrap. Now the rope will unwind using momentum.

MATADOR WHIRL (DF = 2.4)

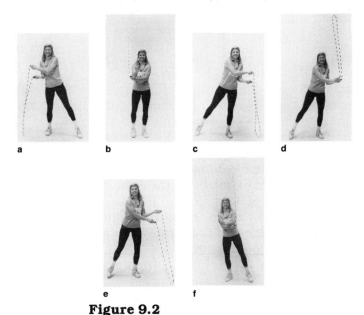

a   b   c   d

e   f

Figure 9.2

This is a difficult technique to explain and illustrate because it closely resembles Figure-Eights. To begin, turn the rope twice to the right side (9.2a). As the rope comes up the second time, cross right hand over the left while bringing the rope across (9.2b). Now, allow the hands to roll over each other while on the left so that the rope makes two circles on that side (9.2c-e). Cross left hand over the right arm as the rope comes up the second time (9.2f) to bring the rope back to the right and repeat as many times as you wish.

Matador Whirls have a very natural feel to them when mastered and often replace Figure-Eights as a transition technique with advanced rope jumpers.

DEMONSTRATOR PROFILE:

Kristin Willman is a mother of two and a member of the National Ropics Precision Team. She finds that Ropics keeps her muscles toned, improves her stamina, and helps keep her weight under control. She says that Ropics also makes for great conversation at parties—"You do what!?"

SAMURAI WHIRL (DF = 2.6)

a   b   c   d

Figure 9.3

The Samurai Whirl is essentially a Figure-Eight done from front to back rather than from side to side. Begin by doing Front Windmills in a counterclockwise direction as you face the rope (9.3a). As the rope begins its ascent (9.3b), bring the right hand over and behind the head so the rope makes one turn in that position (9.3c). As the rope makes its ascent again, bring the right hand back in front (9.3d) to complete the cycle. Samurai Whirls can also be done with the left hand or with both hands.

Gloria Weckwerth is a mother of two children and a member of the National Ropics Precision Team. She began doing aerobic dance because she was getting injured too often playing volleyball. Now she has added Ropics to her exercise options because it is also safe and adds unlimited variety and challenges to her workouts.

WAIST WRAP (DF = 2.7)

Figure 9.4

Begin by doing Overhead Windmills to the right with two hands (9.4a). As the rope comes forward, bring the left hand down behind the back while the right hand circles overhead (9.4b, c). Just as the rope comes around the second time, bring the right hand down to waist level (9.4d) to complete the wrap. To unwrap, lift the right hand overhead again and unwind the rope by reversing direction.

Waist Wraps are often more difficult for experienced rope jumpers to master than novices since two habits must be broken: The rope turns horizontally rather than vertically, and the arms move independently rather than mirroring each other. Once mastered,

Waist Wraps can be initiated directly from other techniques without doing a preliminary Overhead Windmill. Mastering these types of skills is one of the prerequisites to learning how to manipulate a jump rope well.

DEMONSTRATOR PROFILE:

Deborah Solis holds a Master of Fine Arts Degree in dance and found that Ropics improves her endurance for performing in dance concerts. She also discovered that Ropics didn't hurt her knees like running does. Ropics has become her other art form as she performs with her husband Ken in shows around the country.

OPEN STEP-THROUGH (DF = 2.7)

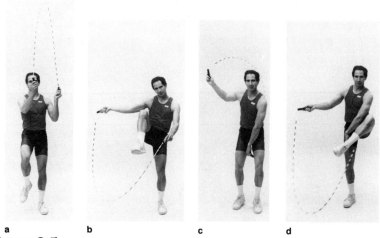

a   b   c   d

Figure 9.5

This technique looks fancy, and as the name implies, one leg steps through the rope at a time. Begin by turning the rope forward with both hands to the left. As the rope comes down, place the left hand between the legs and bring the right hand overhead to turn the rope horizontally (9.5a, c). Lift each leg as the rope approaches it (9.5b, d).

The secret to mastering Step-Throughs is being able to turn the upper half of the rope in a horizontal direction rather than vertically as in jumping. To facilitate learning this technique, it often helps to do a Waist Wrap first. Then, as the rope unwraps, you simply continue turning the hand overhead and place the other hand between the legs. Once mastered, you can approach Open Step-Throughs directly from Figure-Eights and even from an RJT.

CROSSED STEP-THROUGH (DF = 2.8)

Figure 9.6

You execute a Crossed Step-Through just like the open variation, except you cross the arms so that the left hand circles overhead while the right arm is between the legs.

SHOULDER WRAP (DF = 2.8)

Figure 9.7

Do a Side Windmill with the right hand. When the rope begins to come down on one of its turns (9.7a), flex the right wrist and raise the right elbow out to the right side. The rope will come around to wrap the right shoulder (9.7b, c). (If the rope hits your back, you probably need to flex the wrist more or lift the elbow more.) Put the left hand in the way so that the rope also wraps around it. Now you can push the rope away at the end of the wrap to help it unwind (9.7d).

Figures 9.7e and 9.7f show a Shoulder Wrap with the rope turning backward. The main difference from the forward Shoulder Wrap is that you don't lift your elbow as much. Instead, you flex your elbow much like when you make a muscle.

FOOT FLICK (DF = 2.8)

a   b

Figure 9.8

Here's a nice way to get out of a Foot Catch. Lift the foot that caught the rope by flexing the knee (9.8a). Keep tension on the rope by drawing up the arms as you lift the knee. Now, kick forward and flex the foot slightly to release the rope (9.8b). The rope will now travel backward. This is another technique for reversing rope rotation.

Representative Level 2 Rope Jumping Techniques

SIDE STRADDLE (DF = 2.0)

a   b   c   d

Figure 9.9

You can easily learn Side Straddles, also known as jumping jacks, once you understand the timing. The feet must be coming together or just beginning to spread apart when the rope passes underneath the body (9.9b, d). The feet are in contact with the ground and either close together (9.9a) or spread apart (9.9c) when the rope is overhead. Again, work on making each jump light and easy. Fight the tendency to jump high and throw the legs out quickly.

SCISSORS (DF = 2.1)

a   b

Figure 9.10

Scissors duplicate the action of cross-country skiing. On the first jump, split one leg forward and the other leg backward (9.10a). On the next jump, the legs reverse positions (9.10b).

FRONT STRADDLE (DF = 2.2)

a   b   c   d

Figure 9.11

The Front Straddle is like the Scissors except that the legs do not reverse the split with each jump. Instead, the feet are brought together (9.11a, c) between splits (9.11b, d). Therefore, Front Straddles are less strenuous, although they are a little more complicated.

HEEL TOUCHES (DF = 2.3)

a   b   c

Figure 9.12

You can touch the heel of either foot to the front (9.12a), side (9.12b), or across the other leg (9.12c) to the floor. Put combinations of heel touches together to create a little fancy footwork. Remember, the touches to the various sides are completed when the rope is overhead.

TOE TOUCHES (DF = 2.4)

a   b   c   d

Figure 9.13

Between each jump, the toe of either foot can be touched to the front (9.13a), side (9.13b), back (9.13c), or across the other leg (9.13d) to the floor. Toe Touches are a little harder than Heel Touches because the rope more readily snags an extended foot than a flexed foot. Put Toe Touches together in different combinations or combine them with Heel Touches to mimic folk dances like the Irish fling.

DEMONSTRATOR PROFILE:

Heidi Zarder is one of our best Ropics instructors, a member of the National Ropics Precision Team, and a mother of three. Heidi learned Ropics techniques particularly quickly because she worked with other props in the past such as the baton when she was a drum majorette and the rifle when she was a drum and bugle corp member.

KICKS (DF = 2.5)

a   b   c

Figure 9.14

Kicks are much like Toe Touches except that the foot doesn't touch the floor. Instead, you kick one foot out to the side (9.14a), front (9.14b), or across the other leg (9.14c). Combine Kicks with any of the other techniques already described, and you begin to get the idea that the combinations you can create are nearly endless. Develop your own signature combination.

MATADOR OPEN (DF = 2.5)

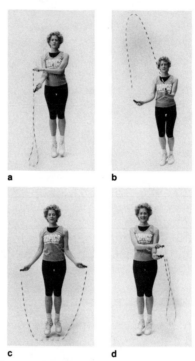

Figure 9.15

The Matador Open is really a two-handed Side Windmill combined with a Two-Foot Jump. Begin by swinging the rope with both hands to one side, in this case the right (9.15a). As the rope approaches the top, bring the left hand back to the left (9.15b) so that the rope opens and then jump over the rope (9.15c). You can repeat the technique by bringing the rope back to the right again or bringing the rope to the left side as shown in Figure 9.15d.

HUSTLE WALK (DF = 2.6)

Figure 9.16

With the Hustle Walk, there's no need to stay in one place while jumping. To do the Hustle Walk, take three shuffles forward beginning on the right foot (9.16a-c). Jump over the rope between each shuffle. After the fourth jump, kick left leg forward (9.16d). Now, shuffle backward (9.16e-g) and kick right leg forward on the fourth jump back (9.16h).

KNEE LIFTS (DF = 2.6)

a   b   c   d

Figure 9.17

Alternately lift knees with every other turn of the rope. To make Knee Lifts look good, point the lifted foot. This technique works the hip flexors. A particularly demanding variation called High Steps requires you to lift alternate knees with *every* turn of the rope much like running in place through tires.

CROSS STEP (DF = 2.6)

a   b

c   d

Figure 9.18

Instead of bringing the feet together as during Side Straddles, cross one leg behind the other (9.18b). On the next turn, split the legs to a straddle position (9.18c). You may cross the opposite leg in front on the third turn (9.18d). This technique develops agility.

SIDE SHUFFLE (DF = 2.7)

a   b   c   d

Figure 9.19

Here's another technique where you get to move. As the name implies, shuffle to the side by slightly lifting the leg that is on the side to which you are moving and scoot a little as you jump over the rope. You can move back to your original position by lifting the opposite leg and scooting the other way.

FRONT CROSS (DF = 2.9)

a   b   c   d

Figure 9.20

Begin Front Crosses by first learning the arm movement without being concerned about jumping over the rope. Place the rope at the heels and swing the rope overhead. As the rope approaches its zenith, begin to cross the arms so that they overlap at mid-forearm by the time the rope is at the toes. Repeat until the action is smooth and the rope would seem to pass under the feet. Common mistakes are to have the arms crossed unequally or to have the handle(s) drooping down rather than pointing out to the side.

When you have mastered the first step, jump over the rope just once keeping the above points in mind. You should begin to un-cross the arms when the rope is overhead again and continue with standard jumping. Figure 9.20 shows the entire sequence. As you gain experience and confidence, you can continuously cross and uncross your arms. Motivate yourself by setting a goal of doing just one more consecutive Front Cross with each practice session. Another challenging variation, called Sustained Front Crosses, is to keep the arms crossed while jumping.

CHAPTER **10**

Level 3 Techniques

By the time you begin to tackle Level 3 techniques, you should be feeling pretty good about your jump rope skills and be in excellent physical condition. With Level 3, we begin to get into the "wow" techniques, which are sure to make you feel accomplished and draw admiring looks. A sample Level 3 workout for a person who has been using Ropics for several months follows on page 110.

Creating Your Own Rope Jumping Techniques

Don't be afraid to create your own variations, techniques, and routines. You'll take exceptional pride in even the slightest variation you can call your own. Any technique is legitimate as long as it can be completed safely and in a smooth, uninterrupted fashion. A few helpful methods for coming up with your own techniques and style are explained in the box on page 111.

The following pages illustrate some intriguing examples at this challenging level. More advanced techniques are particularly difficult to capture with still photos, so consider the Ropics video series described in the appendix if you have trouble visualizing how the technique is executed.

SAMPLE LEVEL 3 ROPICS WORKOUT

Warm-Up

Gradually increase workout intensity over 5 to 10 minutes by alternating intervals of Level 1 and Level 2 LITs with brief intervals of Level 1 RJTs.

Stretching

Spend 5 to 10 minutes stretching using the techniques illustrated on pages 66-70.

Skill Development

Practice the 180-Degree Figure-Eight and Matador Cross, or practice a new technique or combination that you've created.

Aerobic Phase

By now, the aerobic phase should be at least 20 minutes long. Chances are good that you know how your body responds to Ropics and you are able to adjust the exercise intensity without actually looking at the RPE scale. Level 1 and Level 2 RJTs should dominate your RJT intervals because Level 3 RJTs tend to be more demanding. Level 3 RJTs are more or less the spice of a workout and should be used in small measure because they are generally too strenuous in large measure. However, you can add Level 3 LITs as you master them. Because you are quite experienced now, you might even help guide others who are interested in joining you for a top-notch workout.

Cool-Down

Gradually decrease the exercise intensity over 5 minutes by increasing the time spent doing LITs compared to RJTs or switch to light jogging then brisk walking. End the session with some slow stretches to relaxing music.

Good work! Undoubtedly, you are the local jump rope expert now. We hope that you are so hooked on Ropics by now that you will contact us and ask for more.

Creating Your Own Techniques and Style

- **Extrapolation.** Create a technique by seeing if what worked in one situation will work in a similar situation. For example, if you can combine a Side Straddle with a Front Cross, how about combining another footwork variation like a Toe Touch with a Front Cross. Extrapolation can also mean extending the limits a little further. If you can do a Double Under, how about a Triple Under? If you can do a 180-Degree Turn-About, how about a 360-Degree Turn-About?

- **Adaptation.** This is a particularly rich method for creating techniques or variations. In this case, you see if a movement or skill from another discipline can be adapted to rope jumping. To create techniques for Ropics, we have drawn from such diverse sources as karate, footbag, gymnastics, and various forms of dance (even the Argentinian gaucho folk dance).

- **Observation.** Some might claim that observation is "stealing" ideas from others. Actually, in my experience, other jump rope enthusiasts are quite eager to share their favorite techniques, which makes covert observation unnecessary. That's fortunate since this has been the single largest source of new techniques and shows no sign of drying up.

- **Imagination.** This would have to be the most difficult method of creativity to define. It helps, however, to ask "what if" questions like: What if I tried to hold the rope like this? or What if I wrapped the rope around my leg in a Swing Wrap rather than my waist? Perhaps the most important tip is to keep an open mind and be willing to try new things.

- **Dumb Luck.** I hate to admit it, but some of my best techniques were created during a failed attempt at another. For example, I created an Arm Wrap when one arm got in the way while doing Side Windmills. The key to making dumb luck work is recognizing mistakes that have real potential as full-fledged techniques.

Representative Level 3 Low-Impact Techniques

180-DEGREE FIGURE-EIGHT (DF = 3.0)

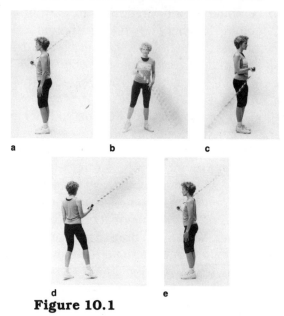

Figure 10.1

This technique is the low-impact version of a 180-Degree Turn-About described later. Turn the rope in a forward direction on the right side (10.1a). Bring the rope over to the left and pivot 180 degrees to the left as the rope comes down (10.1b). After the body turns, the rope will be on the right side again, though turning backward (10.1c). If you wish to return to your original position, bring the rope over to the left side again and pivot 180 degrees in that direction (10.1d). The rope will now be at the right side and turning forward again (10.1e).

OPEN LAYOUT (DF = 3.3)

Figure 10.2

If the video will help you greatly with any technique, it would be with the Open Layout—a difficult one to describe at best. Begin by bringing the rope down to the right side (10.2a). Now, lift and open both arms almost as though you were going into a swan dive (10.2b, c). The rope will go behind your back, and the middle of the rope will touch the floor behind you. Before the rope touches the heels, bring both arms back up and over to the left (10.2d-f).

Representative Level 3 Rope Jumping Techniques

MATADOR CROSS (DF = 3.2)

Figure 10.3

Also known as the Side-Swing Cross, this technique could be viewed as a Side Windmill combined with a Front Cross. Begin by learning just the arm movement. With both hands to the left side, swing the rope in a circle. As the rope approaches its zenith, cross the left arm over the right (the right hand stays at the left side) to bring the rope down to the feet.

When the action is smooth and the rope would seem to pass under the feet, jump over the rope and begin to uncross the arms when the rope is overhead. After the jump you may bring both hands to either side again to repeat the technique. Figure 10.3 shows a Matador Cross to the right.

180-DEGREE TURN-ABOUT (DF = 3.2)

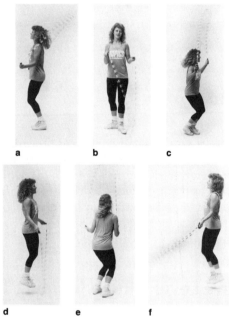

a   b   c

d   e   f

Figure 10.4

(Before learning 180-Degree Turn-Abouts, you should practice 180-Degree Figure-Eights [see page 112] and be adept at jumping with the rope turning backward.)

Hold the rope with both hands; swing the rope over to the left and pivot the body 180 degrees toward the left as the rope comes down (10.4b). When the rope is overhead, you should be facing the opposite direction (10.4c). The rope is now turning backward and comes around to meet the heels. Don't worry about jumping over the rope right away; just practice the arm movement and pivoting.

When the movement feels comfortable, jump over the rope just after pivoting (10.4d). When you have completed the 180-Degree Turn-About, you will be jumping backward. You can return to your original position by swinging the rope to the other side and then pivoting your body 180 degrees to jump forward again (10.4e-f). When you have mastered both phases, you can jump continuously while turning in a circle!

DOUBLE UNDER (DF = 3.5)

a   b   c   d

Figure 10.5

The Double Under (or Double) is especially strenuous to learn, so be certain you are warmed-up, are in good physical condition, and don't have arthritis or other conditions which preclude high-impact exercise.

The coordination required to do a Double Under is the same as a Two-Foot Jump. You need to power the rope more from the arms, however, and jump higher so that the rope spins *twice* around for a jump. You may have a tendency at first to land in a squat position. With a little practice you can land with just a little bend in the knees as shown in Figure 10.5d.

Double Unders can also be done consecutively, one right after the other. The timing and rhythm between the arms and legs is much different than it is with the other techniques taught here, so it usually requires some dogged practice to master.

CHAPTER 11

Further Insights Into Ropics

As mentioned in the preface, *Ropics® : The Next Jump Forward in Fitness* was designed to provide you with a solid foundation of skills and knowledge pertaining to the short jump rope. It is impossible in a normal size book to include every technique possible with this incredibly versatile apparatus or to reveal every nuance of the Ropics program. Table 11.1 begins to illustrate why. Such a wide variety of short rope techniques exist that Ropics divides the two main divisions, RJTs and LITs, into ten smaller categories. Techniques in the same category share some similarity in how they are executed. For example, techniques in the footwork category require you to move your feet in different ways while jumping over the rope. Techniques in the wraps category require you to wrap the rope around some part of your body. Of course, techniques in each category vary in difficulty so they are also placed in their appropriate skill levels. The definitions of the categories and one representative technique for each is shown in Figures 11.1 through 11.10.

FOOTWORK

Figure 11.1   Toe Touches.

The *footwork* category includes techniques where you move your feet in different ways while jumping over the rope.

Table 11.1   **Complete Short Rope Technique Organization**

Division	Category	Level 1	Level 2	Level 3	Level 4	Level 5
			Skill level			
Rope Jumping Technique	Footwork		Toe Touches [a]			
	Crosses		Front Cross [b]			
	Turn-abouts			180-Degree Turn-About [c]		
	Multiples			Double Under [d]		
Low-Impact Technique	Whirls	Figure-Eight [e]				
	Wraps		Waist Wrap [f]			
	Step-throughs			Open Step-Through [g]		
	Catches			Leg Over Pass [h]		
	Bolas			Synchronous Bolas [i]		
Miscellaneous		Foot Flick [j]				

[a] Figure 11.1. [b] Figure 11.2. [c] Figure 11.3. [d] Figure 11.4. [e] Figure 11.5. [f] Figure 11.6. [g] Figure 11.7. [h] Figure 11.8. [i] Figure 11.9. [j] Figure 11.10.

CROSSES

Figure 11.2   Front Cross.

Crosses includes techniques where the hands are on opposite sides of the body while you jump over the rope.

TURN-ABOUTS

Figure 11.3   180-Degree Turn-About.

Turn-abouts includes techniques where you turn around in different ways while jumping over the rope.

MULTIPLES

Figure 11.4   Double Under.

Multiples includes techniques where the rope spins more than once for every jump.

WHIRLS

Figure 11.5   Figure-Eight.

Whirls includes techniques where the rope does not pass under the feet nor come in contact with the body.

WRAPS

Figure 11.6   Waist Wrap.

Wraps includes techniques where the rope is wrapped and un-wrapped around some part of the body.

STEP-THROUGHS

Figure 11.7   Open Step-Through.

Step-throughs includes techniques where the rope passes through one leg at a time.

CATCHES

Figure 11.8   Leg Over Pass.

Catches includes techniques where the rope is grasped or caught in different ways by the hand or foot.

BOLAS

Figure 11.9   Synchronous Bolas.

Bolas includes techniques where the rope is held in the middle while the ends are swung in different ways. (Do not attempt to learn bolas without personal coaching since the swinging handles can cause injury.)

MISCELLANEOUS

Figure 11.10   Foot Flick.

The *miscellaneous* category includes unusual techniques that do not fit into any of the other categories.

I did not reveal the more complete technique structure of Ropics earlier because it might have distracted you from learning the more fundamental lessons about safely and effectively exercising with a jump rope. In the future, I hope to reveal more exciting techniques of every difficulty level. I also plan to discuss ideas that would be particularly interesting to those who want to know more about rope jumping's potential as an exercise and even as a future sport. Here are a few of the topics:

- Further explanation of the fundamental differences between Ropics and traditional rope jumping
- More on how to master jump rope techniques
- Methods of reversing the rope rotation
- Elements of style
- Customizing Ropics to fit the training needs of specific activities
- The vast world of variations like Double Dutch, Chinese Wheel, Egg Beaters, and partner jumping

Until then, good health, stay fit, and have fun.

Appendix

Resources

Jump Rope Organizations

World Jump Rope Association (WJRA)

Even though rope jumping is often associated with children, thousands of adult jump rope enthusiasts exist in the United States alone. Unfortunately, before the WJRA was formed in 1991, adult enthusiasts had difficulty sharing ideas, techniques, experiences, and fellowship. WJRA publishes an informative quarterly newsletter that also offers innovative products related to rope jumping. WJRA anticipates their first national camp and jump rope competition in the spring of 1992. For more information contact

World Jump Rope Association
P.O. Box 80415
Lincoln, NE 68501

American Double Dutch League (ADDL)

ADDL was formed in 1973 by two police detectives, Ulysses Williams and David Walker. It specializes in Double Dutch-style rope jumping competitions and, therefore, attracts young people. They hold regional and national tournaments that attract thousands of contestants from city park and recreation departments, Girl Scout Troops, 4-H clubs, and schools. Unfortunately, I have found this organization repeatedly difficult to contact at

American Double Dutch League
4220 Eads Street, NE
Washington, DC 20019

Canadian Skipping Association (CSA)

Whereas ADDL restricts itself to one style of rope jumping, CSA includes both short rope and Double Dutch styles in its annual regional and national team competitions. Their jump rope camps, which are reasonably priced, teach any style of rope jumping you can imagine. The camps are open to all age groups, although they are designed for and predominantly attended by children. Since Canada is such a large country, CSA holds national camps and competitions in Vermilion, Alberta, and Hamilton, Ontario. For a small membership fee, you can also receive their informative quarterly newsletter. For more information contact

Canadian Skipping Association
804 Cedar Island Drive
Kingsville, Ontario
Canada N9Y 3W4

International Rope Skipping Organization (IRSO)

IRSO is the American counterpart to CSA. Like WJRA and CSA, IRSO has a quarterly newsletter and organizes regional and national camps and competitions targeted for jump rope teams. Their modestly priced national (technically international) camp and competition is held in Greeley, Colorado. Again, enthusiasts of any age are welcome to attend their camps, which teach a broad range of jump rope styles. I must inject a word of caution here, however. What their jump rope teams consider to be intermediate in difficulty would be considered advanced by nearly any adult. For more information contact

International Rope Skipping Organization
P.O. Box 3307
Boulder, CO 80307
303-530-7179

Ropics, Inc.

Founded in 1983, Ropics, Inc., is dedicated to promoting rope jumping to all age groups and to developing high-quality instructional materials and presentations. Ropics, Inc., services include workshops, instructor courses, instructional videos (see below), and professional-caliber entertainment. For more information contact

Ropics, Inc.
P.O. Box 373
Greendale, WI 53129
414-423-1707 (9 a.m. to 5 p.m. Central time)

Jump Rope-Related Accessories

Jump Mat

"Kush-N-Jump" made by Sportime is the only cushion that is especially designed for jumping. (There may be other cushions on the market that I am not aware of.) Most cushions are too spongy for rope jumping. The mat comes in two sizes: 24 × 36 inches for $29.95 and 36 × 48 inches for $59.95 (prices correct at time of printing). I recommend the larger model since the smaller cushion is too restrictive for any footwork variations. To order, call Sportime at 1-800-234-5700.

Segmented Jump Ropes

Lifeline International, Inc., is one of the few manufacturers of quality segmented jump ropes that work particularly well with Ropics. They also make good speed ropes. To find a store near you that carries their line, call 1-800-553-6633. If you wish to order directly, call 1-800-252-5867 (in Wisconsin, call 414-321-0874).

Books with Jump Rope Games

Here are two books with many games and activities for rope jumping that especially suit children:

Awesome Jump Rope Activities Book by Mark Sutherland & Cliff Carnes. To order, contact

Education Company
3949 Linus Way
Carmichael, CA 95608
916-483-8846

Skip to Health by Susan Kalbfleisch, Jo Harris, & Jill Elbourn. To order, contact

Heartbeat Enterprises, Inc.
6655 Dobbin Rd.
Columbia, MD 21045
301-381-8553

Ropics Video Series

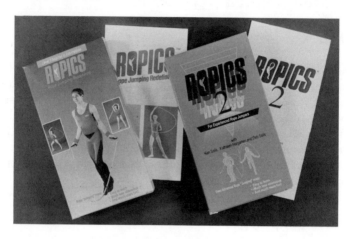

Figure A.1   Ropics video package.

The Ropics video series (Figure A.1) is designed to complement *Ropics® : The Next Jump Forward in Fitness.* The contents of each video are listed in the following paragraphs. Each video is $24.95 + $3.50 shipping and handling (Wisconsin residents add 5.5% sales tax). You can save and get both tapes for $39.95 + $3.50 shipping and handling! (Wisconsin residents add 5.5% sales tax.) To order, call 1-800-252-5867 (in Wisconsin, call 414-321-0874) or write Ropics, Inc.

The Ropics Level 1 Video Includes:

- Step-by-step instruction of the following techniques—Windmills, Figure-Eights, Two-Foot Jump, Jogging Step, Side Straddle, Cross Step, Front Straddles, Scissors, Toe Touches, Heel Touches, Front Cross, Forearm Wrap, Waist Wrap, and Samurai Whirl

- A complete beginners class from warm-up to cool-down and a sample intermediate-level aerobic phase
- Examples of advanced routines and a review of the Ropics approach to rope jumping

The Ropics 2 Video Includes:

- Slow-motion instruction of the remaining techniques taught in this book—Skier, Twist, Leg Over Pass, Swing Wrap, Foot Catch, Side Shuffle, Hustle Walk, Kicks, Matador Open, Knee Lifts, Matador Cross, Matador Whirl, Shoulder Wrap, Foot Flick, Open Layout, Open and Crossed Step-Throughs, 180-Degree Turn-About, 180-Degree Figure-Eight, and Double Under.
- A complete intermediate-advanced follow-along class
- Examples of more advanced routines and further exploration of the Ropics program

Glossary

aerobic—That which uses oxygen. In exercise, refers to activities that predominately depend on energy derived from metabolism that uses oxygen.

aerobic conditioning—Attaining the ability to increase oxygen utilization in order to perform work. Commonly equated with cardiovascular fitness, although skeletal muscle changes are also involved.

agility—The ability to move quickly and accurately while on one's feet.

anaerobic—That which does not use oxygen. In exercise, refers to activities that are so intense that energy needs cannot be predominately met by metabolism that uses oxygen.

backward (rope turning direction)—Turning the rope so that it approaches the heels before the toes.

bolas—Technique category where the middle of the rope is held while the end or ends are turned.

catches—Technique category where the moving rope is grasped by hand or foot where it was not grasped immediately before.

category—Group of techniques related by some similarity in how they are executed.

coordination—The ability to perform complex movement.

crosses—Technique category where the arms are on the opposite sides of the body while jumping over the rope.

dead rope—A jump rope that is not moving nor held tautly.

difficulty factor—A number that indicates approximately how difficult a technique is to execute on a scale of 1.0 to 5.9.

division—A broad class of techniques grouped by whether they require one to jump over the rope or not.

flexibility—The degree of range of motion one has about the joints.

footwork—Technique category where the feet move in varying patterns while jumping over the rope.

forward (rope turning direction)—Turning the rope so that it approaches the toes before the heels.

health—Freedom from disease, injury, or defect.

kinesthetic awareness—The ability to sense where and how parts of the body are positioned and moving in space.

live rope—A jump rope that is moving or held so that there is tension in the rope.

long rope—A jump rope that is typically 14 to 16 feet long and is usually turned by one person on each end while one or more jump over the middle.

Low-Impact Technique (LIT)—A division of techniques that do not require one to jump over the rope. (Also known as Non-Jumping Techniques [NJT] in earlier publications.)

miscellaneous—Technique category that contains techniques that do not fit any of the other categories.

multiples—Technique category where the rope turns more than once for each jump.

osteoporosis—A condition where the bones are weakened due to a loss of calcium.

physical fitness—The ability of one's body to cope with work, exercise, or the environment.

Rated Perceived Exertion scale (RPE scale)—A formal way to communicate how hard you feel you are working on a scale from 0 to 10.

rope artist—One who is concerned with the style as well as the accuracy of technique execution or a routine.

Rope Jumping Technique (RJT)—A division of techniques that requires one to jump over the rope.

Ropics—A proprietary jump rope program that addresses the limitations of traditional rope jumping by making it less strenuous, easier to learn, and more motivating.

short rope—A jump rope that is typically about 9 feet long and is usually turned and jumped over by the same person.

skill level—A group of techniques related by a similar degree of difficulty.

step-throughs—Technique category where the rope passes under one leg at a time.

strength—The ability to generate or accommodate force.

technique—A particular way of manipulating the rope and/or moving the body in relation to the rope. Also referred to as a *trick*.

timing—The ability to move the correct way at the right moment.

trick—See *technique*.

turn-abouts—Technique category where the participant faces another direction while jumping over the rope.

variation—A jump rope technique that varies from another technique in the direction or side from which it is executed or in some other minor way.

whirls—Technique category where the rope does not come in contact with nor pass under the legs.

wraps—Technique category where the rope is wrapped and subsequently unwrapped in an orderly fashion around some portion of the body.

Selected Bibliography

Alter, J. (1986). *Stretch & strengthen*. Boston: Houghton Mifflin.

Alter, M.J. (1988). *Science of stretching*. Champaign, IL: Human Kinetics.

Alter, M.J. (1990). *Sport stretch*. Champaign, IL: Leisure Press.

Anderson, B. (1985). *Stretching*. Bolinas, CA: Shelter.

Baker, J. (1968). Comparison of rope skipping and jogging as methods of improving cardiovascular efficiency of college men. *Research Quarterly*, **39**, 240-243.

Borg, G. (1985). *An introduction to Borg's RPE-scale*. Ithaca, NY: Mouvement.

Coyle, E. (1990). Detraining and retention of training-induced adaptations. *Sports Science Exchange*, **2**.

Getchell, B., & Cleary, C. (1980). The caloric cost of rope skipping and running. *The Physician and Sportsmedicine*, **7**, 56-60.

Groves, D. (1988). Is childhood obesity related to TV addiction? *The Physician and Sportsmedicine*, **16**, 116-122.

Hanson, M.R., Torrence, T., Hungerford, C.W., Smith, P., & Cendali, R. (1983). *Jump for the health of it*. Dallas, TX: American Heart Association.

Jette, M., Mongeon, J., & Routhier, R. (1979). Energy cost of rope skipping. *Journal of Sports Medicine and Physical Fitness*, **19**, 33-37.

Kalbfleisch, S. (1985). *Jump!* New York: Morrow.

McArdle, W., Katch, F., & Katch, V. (1986). *Exercise physiology: Energy, nutrition and human performance*. Philadelphia: Lea & Febiger.

Mylander, M. (1990). Fat City, U.S.A. *Sports Illustrated*, May 21, p. S16.

Nike, Inc. (1988). Sport research review. *The Physician and Sportsmedicine*, **16**, Special Advertising Section.

Paffenbarger, Jr., R., Hyde, R., & Wing, A. (1986). Physical activity, all cause mortality, and longevity of college alumni. *New England Journal of Medicine*, **314**, 605-613.

Sanborn, C. (1990). Exercise, calcium, and bone density. *Sports Science Exchange*, **2**.

Shephard, R. (1989). Prescribing exercise for the senior citizen: Some simple guidelines. In Shephard, R., Anderson, J., et al. (Eds.) *1989 year book of sports medicine* (pp. xv-xxiii). Chicago: Year Book Medical.

Simmons, K. (1988). Are American children really unfit? *The Physician and Sportsmedicine*, **16**, 146-154.

Smith, P. (1981). *Aerobic rope skipping*. Freeport, NY: Educational Activities.

Solis, K., Foster, C., Thompson, N., & Cefalu, C. (1988). Aerobic requirements for and heart rate responses to variations in rope jumping techniques. *The Physician and Sportsmedicine*, **16**, 121-128.

About the Author

Ken Solis (pictured on the back cover) is a physician who recognizes the benefits of rope jumping. An advanced rope artist, he holds the Guinness World Record for jumping the most consecutive double jumps with a cross. He founded the Ropics program to help develop rope jumping as an exercise, sport, and art.

Dr. Solis is an emergency room physician at Watertown Memorial Hospital in Watertown, WI, and a member of the Alpha Omega Alpha medical honor society. His research on aerobic requirements and heart rate responses to various rope jumping techniques was presented at the Pan American Sports Medicine Congress.